Childcraft

STORYTELLING AND OTHER POEMS

Childcraft

IN FIFTEEN VOLUMES

•

VOLUME TWO

STORYTELLING AND OTHER POEMS

FIELD ENTERPRISES EDUCATIONAL CORPORATION
Merchandise Mart Plaza • Chicago 54, Illinois

ACKNOWLEDGMENTS

The publishers of CHILDCRAFT gratefully acknowledge the courtesy of the following publishers and authors for permission to use copyrighted stories, poems, and illustrations:

Bobbs-Merrill Company: "When the Frost Is on the Punkin," from *Neighborly Poems* by James Whitcomb Riley, copyright 1891 and 1919; "A Nonsense Rhyme" and "The Raggedy Man," from *Rhymes of Childhood*, copyright 1890 and 1918 by Riley.

Brandt & Brandt: "Wonder Where This Horseshoe Went," from "From A Very Little Sphinx" in *Poems Selected for Young People* by Edna St. Vincent Millay, published by Harper & Brothers, copyright 1923 by Edna St. Vincent Millay; "Afternoon on a Hill," from *Renascence and Other Poems* by Edna St. Vincent Millay, published by Harper & Brothers, copyright 1917 by Edna St. Vincent Millay; "Western Wagons" and "Daniel Boone," from *A Book of Americans* by Rosemary and Stephen Vincent Benét, published by Rinehart & Company, Inc., copyright 1933 by Rosemary and Stephen Vincent Benét; "It Was," from *Here, There, and Everywhere*, copyright 1927, 1928, by Dorothy Aldis, courtesy A. P. Putnam's Sons.

Child Life magazine publishers and the authors for the following poems: "Look at the Snow" by Mary Carolyn Davies; "Silver Trees" and "Benjamin Jones Goes Swimming" by Aileen Fisher; "The Beech Tree" and "The Little Tune" by Rose Fyleman, and courtesy Society of Authors; "Fun" by Leroy F. Jackson; "The Mocking Bird" by Maurice Lesemann; "A Book" by Adelaide Love; "Tomorrow" by Dorothy Brown Thompson; "The Romp," "Washington," and "Lincoln" by Nancy Byrd Turner; Mrs. Arthur Guiterman for "Pet Show" by Arthur Guiterman; Cloyd Head for "Moving" by Eunice Tietjens; Mark C. Keller for "Little Joe Tunney" by Rebecca McCann; Elizabeth C. Lindsay for "The Magnanimous Sun" by Vachel Lindsay; Clifford Meigs for "The Snow Man," "Johnny Fife and Johnny's Wife," and "The Organ Grinders' Garden" by Mildred Plew Meigs; The Estate of Laura E. Richards for "The Cave-Boy," "Talents Differ," "The Buffalo," and "Antonio" by Laura E. Richards.

Curtis Brown, Ltd.: "Jonathan Bing" and "A New Song to Sing about Jonathan Bing," from *Jonathan Bing and Other Verses* by Beatrice Curtis Brown, published by Oxford University Press of New York. Copyright 1936 by Beatrice Curtis Brown.

Burgess, Gelett: "The Purple Cow," from *The Burgess Nonsense Book* by Gelett Burgess, published by F. A. Stokes Company, New York.

D. Appleton-Century Company and St. Nicholas: "A Ballad of China" by Laura E. Richards.

Dodd, Mead & Company: "Dawn" by Paul Laurence Dunbar, from *The Complete Poems of Paul Laurence Dunbar*, copyright 1896 by Dodd, Mead & Company; "The Vagabond Song," by Bliss Carman, and courtesy of McClelland and Stewart.

Doubleday & Company: "The Camel's Hump," from *Just So Stories* by Rudyard Kipling, copyright 1912, and courtesy A. P. Watt & Sons; "Sometimes," from *The Fairy Flute* by Rose Fyleman, copyright 1923 by Doubleday & Company.

Gerald Duckworth & Company, Ltd.: "The Vulture," from *The Bad Child's Book of Beasts* by Hilaire Belloc.

E. P. Dutton & Company: "The Night Will Never Stay," from *Gipsy and Ginger* by Eleanor Farjeon; "Spring Morning" and "Hoppity," from *When We Were Very Young* by A. A. Milne, and courtesy A. A. Milne, Curtis Brown, Ltd., and Methuen & Company, Ltd.

Flexman, John: "The Shiny Little House" by Nancy M. Hayes.

Harcourt, Brace & Company: "Wheels and Wings" and "When Young Melissa Sweeps," from *Magpie Lane* by Nancy Byrd Turner, copyright 1927 by Harcourt.

Harper & Brothers: Stanzas from "The Wakeupworld," from *The Lost Zoo* by Countee Cullen, copyright 1940 by Harper & Brothers.

Henry Holt & Company: "Bluebells," "Sleepyhead," and "Miss T," from *Collected Poems* by Walter de la Mare, copyright 1920 by Henry Holt & Company, and courtesy Walter de la Mare; "The Pasture," from *North of Boston* by Robert Frost; "Theme in Yellow" and "Fog," from *Chicago Poems* by Carl Sandburg; "Loveliest of Trees," from *A Shropshire Lad* by A. E. Housman, and courtesy of The Society of Authors as the Literary Representative of the Trustees of the Estate of the late A. E. Housman, and Jonathan Cape, Ltd., publishers of A. E. Housman's *Collected Poems*.

Jackson, Leroy F.: "Fun," and "Grandpa Dropped His Glasses."

Jones, J. Morris: "To a Firefly," "Christmas Eve," and "Christmas Day."

Knopf, Alfred A.: "Rebecca" and "The Yak," from *Cautionary Verses* by Hilaire Belloc, copyright 1931 by Hilaire Belloc and courtesy Gerald Duckworth and Co., Ltd.; "Cumberland Gap" from *America Sings* by Carl Carmer.

J. B. Lippincott Company: "Song for a Little House," from *The Rocking Horse*, copyright 1919, 1946 by Christopher Morley; "The Highwayman" from *Collected Poems, Volume I*, by Alfred Noyes, copyright 1906 by Alfred Noyes, and courtesy of the author; "The Pilgrims Came," "The Telegraph," and "A Letter Is a Gypsy Elf," from *For Days and Days* by Annette Wynne, copyright 1919 by Lippincott; "Ring Around the World," from *All Through the Year* by Annette Wynne, copyright 1932 by Annette Wynne; "City Streets and Country Roads," from *Joan's Door* by Eleanor Farjeon, copyright 1926 by Lippincott.

Little, Brown & Company: "Kite-Weather," from *Jane, Joseph, and John: Their Book of Verse* by Ralph Bergengren; "To the Little Girl Who Wriggles," "The Umbrella Brigade," "Alice's Supper," and "Eletelephony," from *Tirra Lirra* by Laura E. Richards, copyright 1918, 1930, 1932 by Laura E. Richards.

MacDonald, Maurice: "The Wind and the Moon" by George MacDonald.

The Macmillan Company: "Frolic," from *Collected Poems* by A. E. (G. Russell), and courtesy Diarmuid Russell; "A Summer Morning," from *The Pointed People* by Rachel Field; "The Potatoes Dance," "Yet Gentle Will the Griffin Be," and "The Mysterious Cat," from *Collected Poems* by Vachel Lindsay; "Sea Fever," from *Poems* by John Masefield, and courtesy John Masefield and The Society of Authors; "White Fields" and "April Showers," from *Collected Poems* by James Stephens, courtesy of the author; "April" and "May Night," from *Collected Poems* by Sara Teasdale.

Meigs, Mildred Plew: "Pirate Don Durk of Dowdee."

Miller, Juanita J.: "Columbus" by Joaquin Miller.

The Mosher Press: "A Christmas Folk Song," from *A Wayside Lute* by Lizette Woodworth Reese.

G. P. Putnam's Sons: "It Was," from *Here, There, ond Everywhere* by Dorothy Aldis, copyright 1927, 1928 by Dorothy Aldis.

Sayers, Frances Clarke: "Who Calls?"

Charles Scribner's Sons: "The Dog," from *Kitten's Garden of Verses by Oliver Herford*, copyright 1911 by Oliver Herford, 1939 by Beatrice Herford Hayward.

Small, Maynard & Company: "A Vagabond Song" by Bliss Carman.

Smith, Fredrika Shumway: "The Popcorn Man."

The Viking Press: "Mary," from *Bells and Grass* by Walter de la Mare, copyright 1942 by Walter de la Mare, and courtesy of the author; "The Circus," from *Under the Tree* by Elizabeth Madox Roberts, copyright 1922 by B. W. Huebsch, Inc.

Walt Disney Productions and Western Printing and Lithographing Company of Racine, Wis., for illustrations on pages 94 and 95. All rights reserved by Walt Disney Productions throughout the world.

CONTENTS

POEMS FOR EVERY DAY

HUMOROUS POEMS

STORYTELLING POEMS AND BALLADS

A BOOK

A BOOK, I think, is very like
A little golden door
That takes me into places
Where I've never been before.

It leads me into fairyland
Or countries strange and far.
And, best of all, the golden door
Always stands ajar.

ADELAIDE LOVE

ONLY ONE MOTHER

HUNDREDS of stars in the pretty sky,
  Hundreds of shells on the shore together,
Hundreds of birds that go singing by,
  Hundreds of lambs in the sunny weather.

Hundreds of dewdrops to greet the dawn,
  Hundreds of bees in the purple clover,
Hundreds of butterflies on the lawn,
  But only one mother the wide world over.

GEORGE COOPER

12

IT WAS

WHEN he came to tuck me in
    And pat me on the head
He tried to guess (he always does)
Who was in my bed.

"Is it Sally?" he guessed first,
"Or her sister Joan?
It's such a wriggling little girl
It couldn't be my own.

"It can't be Mary Ann," he said,
"Or Deborah because
All their eyes are much too blue—
My goodness me, I think it's you!"
And he was right. It was.

DOROTHY ALDIS

SONG FOR A LITTLE HOUSE

I'M GLAD our house is a little house,
  Not too tall nor too wide:
I'm glad the hovering butterflies
  Feel free to come inside.

Our little house is a friendly house.
  It is not shy or vain;
It gossips with the talking trees,
  And makes friends with the rain.

And quick leaves cast a shimmer of green
  Against our whited walls,
And in the phlox, the courteous bees
  Are paying duty calls.

                    CHRISTOPHER MORLEY

14

WHEN YOUNG MELISSA SWEEPS

WHEN young Melissa sweeps a room
    I vow she dances with the broom!

She curtsies in a corner brightly
And leads her partner forth politely.

Then up and down in jigs and reels,
With gold dust flying at their heels,

They caper.   With a whirl or two
They make the wainscot shine like new;

They waltz beside the hearth, and quick
It brightens, shabby brick by brick.

A gay gavotte across the floor,
A Highland fling from door to door,

And every crack and corner's clean
Enough to suit a dainty queen.

If ever you are full of gloom,
Just watch Melissa sweep a room!

                NANCY BYRD TURNER

THE SHINY LITTLE HOUSE

I WISH, how I wish, that I had a little house,
  With a mat for the cat and a hole for the mouse,
And a clock going "tock" in a corner of the room
And a kettle, and a cupboard, and a big birch broom.

To school in the morning the children off would run,
And I'd give them a kiss and a penny and a bun.
But directly they had gone from this little house of mine,
I'd clap my hands and snatch a cloth,
    and shine, shine, shine.

I'd shine all the knives, all the windows and the floors,
All the grates, all the plates,
    all the handles on the doors,
Every fork, every spoon, every lid, and every tin,
Till everything was shining like a new bright pin.

At night, by the fire, when the children were in bed,
I'd sit and I'd knit, with a cap upon my head,
And the kettles, and the saucepans they would
    shine, shine, shine,
In this tweeny little, cosy little house of mine!

NANCY M. HAYES

16

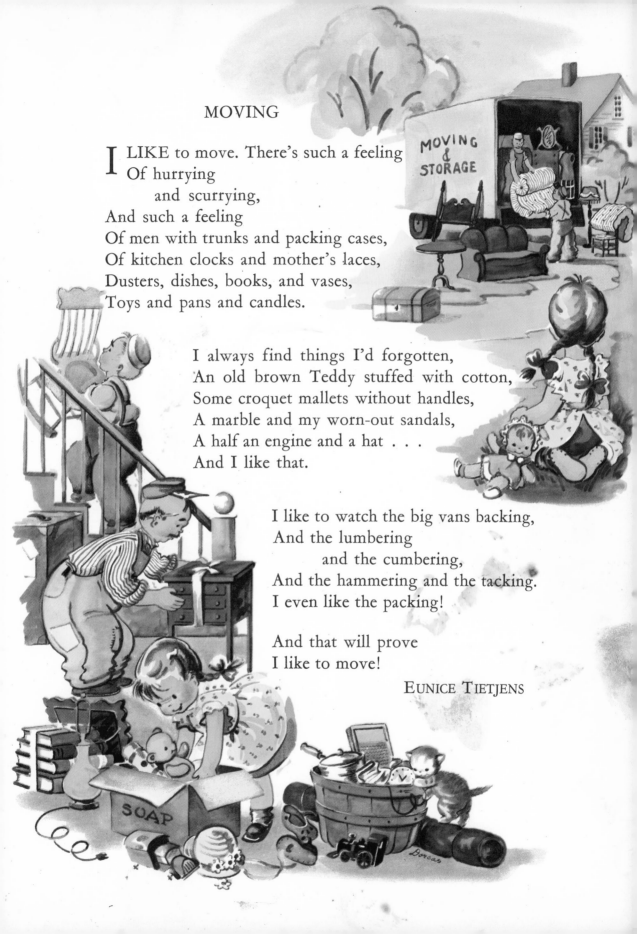

MOVING

I LIKE to move. There's such a feeling
    Of hurrying
        and scurrying,
And such a feeling
Of men with trunks and packing cases,
Of kitchen clocks and mother's laces,
Dusters, dishes, books, and vases,
Toys and pans and candles.

I always find things I'd forgotten,
An old brown Teddy stuffed with cotton,
Some croquet mallets without handles,
A marble and my worn-out sandals,
A half an engine and a hat . . .
And I like that.

I like to watch the big vans backing,
And the lumbering
        and the cumbering,
And the hammering and the tacking.
I even like the packing!

And that will prove
I like to move!

EUNICE TIETJENS

SLEEPYHEAD

As I LAY awake in the white moonlight,
I heard a faint singing in the wood,
  "Out of bed,
  Sleepyhead,
  Put your white foot now,
  Here we are,
  Beneath the tree
  Singing round the root now!"

I looked out of the window, in the white moonlight,
The trees were like snow in the wood—
    "Come away,
    Child, and play
    Light with the gnomies;
    In a mound,
    Green and round,
    That's where their home is.

    "Honey sweet,
    Curds to eat,
    Cream and fruménty,
    Shells and beads,
    Poppy seeds,
    You shall have plenty."

But as soon as I stooped in the dim moonlight
To put on my stocking and my shoe,
The sweet sweet singing died sadly away,
And the light of the morning peeped through:
Then instead of the gnomies there came a red robin
To sing of the buttercups and dew.

WALTER DE LA MARE

18

YET GENTLE WILL THE GRIFFIN BE

(What Grandpa Told the Children)

THE MOON? It is a griffin's egg,
  Hatching tomorrow night.
And how the little boys will watch
With shouting and delight
To see him break the shell and stretch
And creep across the sky.
The boys will laugh. The little girls,
I fear, may hide and cry.
Yet gentle will the griffin be,
Most decorous and fat,
And walk up to the Milky Way
And lap it like a cat.

VACHEL LINDSAY

THE NIGHT WILL NEVER STAY

THE night will never stay,
  The night will still go by,
Though with a million stars
  You pin it to the sky.
Though you bind it with the blowing wind
  And buckle it with the moon,
The night will slip away
  Like sorrow or a tune.

ELEANOR FARJEON

MORNING

WILL there really be a morning?
Is there such a thing as day?
Could I see it from the mountains
If I were as tall as they?
Has it feet like water-lilies?
Has it feathers like a bird?
Is it brought from famous countries
Of which I've never heard?
Oh, some scholar! Oh, some sailor!
Oh, some wise man from the skies!
Please to tell a little pilgrim
Where the place called *morning* lies!

EMILY DICKINSON

DAWN

AN ANGEL, robed in spotless white,
Bent down and kissed the sleeping Night.
Night woke to blush; the sprite was gone.
Men saw the blush and called it Dawn.

PAUL LAURENCE DUNBAR

SONG OF THE WAKEUPWORLD

"WAKE up, O World; O World, awake!
  The light is bright on hill and lake;
O World, awake; wake up, O World!
The flags of the wind are all unfurled;
Wake up, O World; O World, awake!
Of earth's delightfulness partake.

Wake up, O World, whatever hour;
Sweet are the fields, sweet is the flower!
Wake up, O World; O World, awake;
Perhaps to see the daylight break,
Perhaps to see the sun descend,
The night begin, the daylight end.

But something surely to behold,
Not bought with silver or with gold,
Not shown in any land of dreams.
For open eyes the whole world teems
With lovely things to do or make,
Wake up, O World; O World, awake!"

COUNTEE CULLEN

21

MARY

MARY! Mary! *Mary!*
 Come to the dairy, please!
Give me some butter to spread on my bread,
Give me a morsel of cheese.
The cows in the meadow are chewing the cud,
Some of them deep in the stream—
Give me a suppet of curds and whey,
Or a wee little bowl of cream!
It's half a week since breakfast,
And cook won't spare a crumb;
Fol-di-diddle-O, starve I shall,
Unless, you dear, you come!
A hungry wolf's inside me,
Though I wouldn't for worlds just tease;
Mary! Mary! *Mary!*
Come to the dairy, *please!*

                    WALTER DE LA MARE

MISS T.

IT'S a very odd thing—
  As odd as can be—
That whatever Miss T. eats
  Turns into Miss T.;
Porridge and apples,
  Mince, muffins and mutton,
Jam, junket, jumbles—
  Not a rap, not a button
It matters; the moment
  They're out of her plate,
Though shared by Miss Butcher
  And sour Mr. Bate;
Tiny and cheerful,
  And neat as can be,
Whatever Miss T. eats
  Turns into Miss T.

WALTER DE LA MARE

23

PET SHOW

WE had a pet show out on our lawn,
    And one little girl brought a real, live fawn,
And one small boy dragged a black bull calf,
And another had a coon that would make you laugh.
There were twelve nice dogs with well-groomed coats,
Twenty-two kittens with bows at their throats,
A turtle and a frog from Silver Lake,
A goldfish, a pony, and a garter snake,
Five red hens and four Plymouth Rocks
And six tiny lizards in a cardboard box.
They were shown by children of various sizes
Who all had ice cream and all won prizes.

ARTHUR GUITERMAN

WINGS AND WHEFLS

AHOY and ahoy, birds!
We cannot have wings
And feathers and things,
But dashing on wheels
With the wind at our heels
Is almost like flying—
Such joy, birds!

Oho and Oho, birds!
Of course we can't rise
Up and up to the skies;
But skimming and sliding
On rollers, and gliding,
Is almost as jolly,
You know, birds!

NANCY BYRD TURNER

25

KITE WEATHER

To the South the geese are going.
Across the world a breeze is blowing—
Blowing leaves from every tree,
Blowing ships upon the sea,
Blowing hats off people's heads,
Blowing chimney smoke to threads,
Blowing till the curtain flutters,
Slamming doors, and shaking shutters.
Then's the time to fly your kite,
But you have to hold it tight.

Blow, breeze, blow!
   And lift your kite along.
Blow, breeze, blow!
   The string is stout and strong.
Just a little harder blow,
Up and up we, too, would go.
People would look up and stare,
Seeing children in the air.

To the South the geese are going.
Across the world a breeze is blowing—
Blowing something, it is clear,
Into me that's wild and queer.
I could dance, and kick, and caper
Like my kite that's only paper.
I *enjoy* to feel the string
Pull and tug like anything.
A living kite it seems to be,
And tries to fly away with me.

Blow, breeze, blow!
   And lift our kite along.
Blow, breeze, blow!
   The string is stout and strong.
Just a little harder blow,
And the people down below
Would look up at us and say,
"There's a kite that's run away!"

RALPH BERGENGREN

THE CIRCUS

FRIDAY came and the circus was there,
  And Mother said that the twins and I
And Charles and Clarence and all of us
  Could go out and see the parade go by.

And there were wagons with pictures on,
  And you never could guess what they had inside,
Nobody could guess, for the doors were shut,
  And there was a dog that a monkey could ride.

A man on the top of a sort of a cart
  Was clapping his hands and making a talk.
And the elephant came—he can step pretty far—
  It made us laugh to see him walk.

Three beautiful ladies came riding by,
  And each one had on a golden dress,
And each one had a golden whip.
  They were queens of Sheba, I guess.

A big wild man was in a cage,
  And he had some snakes going over his feet.
And somebody said, "He eats them alive!"
  But I didn't see him eat.

ELIZABETH MADOX ROBERTS

THE POPCORN MAN

I LIKE to meet the popcorn man.
  His house just rolls along,
And always after school is out
We gather in a throng.

There is a stove inside his house
That puffs steam through the top,
And then a snowy shower comes
And corn begins to pop.

We like to hear the popcorn man
Come whistling down the street;
For popcorn balls, with butter sauce,
Are very good to eat.

FREDRIKA SHUMWAY SMITH

THE CAVE-BOY

I DREAMED I was a cave-boy
  And lived in a cave,
A mammoth for my saddle horse,
  A monkey for my slave.
And through the tree-fern forests
  A-riding I would go,
When I was once a cave-boy,
  A million years ago.

I dreamed I was a cave-boy;
  I hunted with a spear
The sabre-toothèd tiger,
  The prehistoric deer.
A wolf-skin for my dress suit,
  I thought me quite a beau,
When I was once a cave-boy,
  A million years ago.

LEONARD
WEISGARD

I dreamed I was a cave-boy;
  My dinner was a bone,
And how I had to fight for it,
  To get it for my own!
We banged each other o'er the head,
  And oft our blood did flow,
When I was once a cave-boy,
  A million years ago.

I dreamed I was a cave-boy.
  The torches' smoky light
Shone on the dinner table,
  A pile of bones so white.
I lapped some water from the spring,
  The easiest way, you know,
When I was once a cave-boy,
  A million years ago.

I dreamed—but now I am awake;
  A voice is in my ear.
"Come out and have a game of ball!
  The sun is shining clear.
We'll have some doughnuts afterwards,
  And then a-swimming go!"
I'm glad I'm *not* a cave-boy,
  A million years ago!

LAURA E. RICHARDS

SOMETIMES

SOME days are fairy days.
  The minute that you wake
You have a magic feeling
  that you never could mistake;
You may not see the fairies,
  but you know that they're about,
And any single minute they
  might all come popping out;
You want to laugh, you want to sing,
  you want to dance and run,
Everything is different,
  everything is fun;
The sky is full of fairy clouds,
  the streets are fairy ways—
Anything might happen
  on truly fairy days.

Some nights are fairy nights.
  Before you go to bed
You hear their darling music
  go chiming in your head;
You look into the garden,
  and through the misty grey
You see the trees all waiting
  in a breathless kind of way.
All the stars are smiling;
  they know that very soon
The fairies will come singing
  from the land behind the moon.
If only you could keep awake
  when Nurse puts out the light . . .
Anything might happen
  on a truly fairy night.

ROSE FYLEMAN

BLUEBELLS

WHERE the bluebells and the wind are,
　　Fairies in a ring I spied,
And I heard a little linnet
　　Singing near beside.

Where the primrose and the dew are,
　　Soon were sped the fairies all:
Only now the green turf freshens,
　　And the linnets call.

WALTER DE LA MARE

THE LITTLE TUNE

HE played his little tune
　　One summer afternoon,
And on the grassy hill
The very breeze was still,
While every buttercup
Looked up—looked up.

He played his little tune
Beneath the yellow moon;
So sweet it was, so light,
That (oh, the darling sight)
The bunnies all drew near
To hear—to hear.

ROSE FYLEMAN

STARBUCK

WONDER WHERE THIS HORSESHOE WENT

WONDER where this horseshoe went.
  Up and down, up and down,
Up and past the monument,
Maybe into town.

Wait a minute. "Horseshoe,
How far have you been?"
Says it's been to Salem
And halfway to Lynn.

Wonder who was in the team.
Wonder what they saw.
Wonder if they passed a bridge—
Bridge with a draw.

Says it went from one bridge
Straight upon another.
Says it took a little girl
Driving with her mother.

                    EDNA ST. VINCENT MILLAY

Nino Carbe

CITY STREETS AND COUNTRY ROADS

THE CITY has streets—
 But the country has roads.
In the country one meets
 Blue carts with their loads
Of sweet-smelling hay,
 And mangolds, and grain:
Oh, take me away
 To the country again!

In the city one sees
 Big trams rattle by,
And the breath of the chimneys
 That blot out the sky,
And all down the pavements
 Stiff lamp-posts one sees—
But the country has hedgerows,
 The country has trees.

As sweet as the sun
 In the country is rain:
Oh, take me away
 To the country again!

ELEANOR FARJEON

35

THE TELEGRAPH

THE WIRES spread out far and wide,
   And cross the town and countryside,
They cross through deserts and through snows,
And pass the spots where no one goes.

But though no feet go out that way
A million words go every day;
Along the wires everywhere
A million words flash through the air.

And if we're happy, if we're well,
The wires far away can tell,
The little words can cross all space
And talk to friends in any place.

ANNETTE WYNNE

HAPPY BIRTHDAY
CONGRATULATIONS
ARRIVED SAFELY
LETTER FOLLOWS

RING AROUND THE WORLD

RING around the world
  Taking hands together
All across the temperate
And the torrid weather.
Past the royal palm-trees
By the ocean sand
Make a ring around the world
Taking each other's hand;
In the valleys, on the hill,
Over the prairie spaces,
There's a ring around the world
Made of children's friendly faces.

ANNETTE WYNNE

A LETTER IS A GYPSY ELF

A LETTER is a gypsy elf
  It goes where I would go myself;
East or West or North, it goes,
Or South past pretty bungalows,
Over mountain, over hill,
Any place it must and will,
It finds good friends that live so far
You cannot travel where they are.

ANNETTE WYNNE

SEA FEVER

I MUST go down to the seas again,
   to the lonely sea and the sky,
And all I ask is a tall ship
   and a star to steer her by,
And the wheel's kick and the wind's song
   and the white sail's shaking,
And the gray mist on the sea's face
   and a gray dawn breaking.

I must go down to the seas again,
   for the call of the running tide
Is a wild call and a clear call
   that may not be denied;
And all I ask is a windy day
   with the white clouds flying,
And the flung spray and the blown spume,
   and the seagulls crying.

I must go down to the seas again,
   to the vagrant gypsy life,
To the gull's way and the whale's way
   where the wind's like a whetted knife;
And all I ask is a merry yarn
   from a laughing fellow-rover,
And a quiet sleep and a sweet dream
   when the long trick's over.

JOHN MASEFIELD

THE SEA GYPSY

I AM fevered with the sunset,
  I am fretful with the bay,
For the wander-thirst is on me
And my soul is in Cathay.

There's a schooner in the offing,
With her topsails shot with fire,
And my heart has gone aboard her
For the islands of Desire.

I must forth again tomorrow!
With the sunset I must be
Hull down on the trail of rapture
In the wonder of the Sea.

RICHARD HOVEY

39

JAY HYDE BARNUM

THE YEAR'S AT THE SPRING

THE year's at the spring
  And the day's at the morn;
Morning's at seven;
The hillside's dew-pearled;
The lark's on the wing;
The snail's on the thorn:
God's in his Heaven—
All's right with the world!

ROBERT BROWNING

GROWING IN THE VALE

GROWING in the vale
  By the uplands hilly,
Growing straight and frail,
  Lady Daffadowndilly.
In a golden crown,
And a scant green gown
    While the spring blows chilly,
    Lady Daffadown,
    Sweet Daffadowndilly.

CHRISTINA ROSSETTI

40

APRIL SHOWERS

THE LEAVES are fresh after the rain,
  The air is sweet and clear,
The sun is shining warm again,
The sparrows hopping in the lane
Are brisk and full of cheer.

And that is why we dance and play,
And that is why we sing,
Calling out in voices gay,
We will not go to school today
Nor learn anything!

It is a happy thing, I say,
To be alive on such a day.

JAMES STEPHENS

APRIL

THE ROOFS are shining from the rain,
  The sparrows twitter as they fly,
And with a windy April grace
  The little clouds go by.

Yet the back yards are bare and brown
  With only one unchanging tree—
I could not be so sure of Spring
  Save that it sings in me.

SARA TEASDALE

Robert McCloskey

SPRING MORNING

WHERE am I going? I don't quite know.
　　Down to the stream where the king-cups grow—
Up on the hill where the pine trees blow—
Anywhere, anywhere. *I* don't know.

Where am I going? The clouds sail by,
Little ones, baby ones, over the sky.
Where am I going? The shadows pass,
Little ones, baby ones, over the grass.

If you were a cloud, and sailed up there,
You'd sail on water as blue as air,
And you'd see me here in the fields and say:
"Doesn't the sky look green today?"

Where am I going? The high rooks call:
"It's awful fun to be born at all."
Where am I going? The ring-doves coo:
"We do have beautiful things to do."

If you were a bird, and lived on high,
You'd lean on the wind when the wind came by,
You'd say to the wind when it took you away:
"That's where I wanted to go today!"

Where am I going? I don't quite know.
What does it matter where people go?
Down to the wood where the bluebells grow—
Anywhere, anywhere. *I* don't know.

                                    A. A. MILNE

HOPPITY

CHRISTOPHER ROBIN goes
    Hoppity, hoppity,

Hoppity, hoppity, hop.
Whenever I tell him
Politely to stop it, he
Says he can't possibly stop.

If he stopped hopping,
    he couldn't go anywhere,
Poor little Christopher
Couldn't go anywhere . . .
That's why he *always* goes

Hoppity, hoppity,
Hoppity,
Hoppity,
Hop.

                    A. A. MILNE

WHO CALLS?

"LISTEN, children, listen,
     won't you come into the night?
The stars have set their candle gleam,
   the moon her lantern light.
I'm piping little tunes for you
   to catch your dancing feet.
There's glory in the heavens,
   but there's magic in the street.
There's jesting here and carnival:
   the cost of a balloon
Is an ancient rhyme said backwards,
   and a wish upon the moon.
The city walls and city streets!
   You shall make of these
As fair a thing as country roads
   and blossomy apple trees."
"What watchman calls us in the night,
   and plays a little tune
That turns our tongues to talking
   now of April, May, and June?
Who bids us come with nimble feet
   and snapping fingertips?"
"I am the Spring, the Spring, the Spring
   with laughter on my lips."

FRANCES CLARKE SAYERS

44

FROLIC

THE CHILDREN were shouting together
  And racing along the sands,
A glimmer of dancing shadows,
A dovelike flutter of hands.

The stars were shouting in heaven,
The sun was chasing the moon;
The game was the same as the children's,
They danced to the self-same tune.

The whole of the world was merry,
One joy from the vale to the height,
Where the blue woods of twilight encircled
The lovely lawns of the light.
                    A. E. (G. W. RUSSELL)

TO A FIREFLY

STARS are twinkling up on high,
  Moon hangs low in eastern sky;
These with thee do not compare,
  Cheerful beacon of the air.

Speeding onward through the dark,
  Beneath the oak trees in the park,
With thy glowing, gleaming light,
  Happy lightning bug of night.
                    J. MORRIS JONES

45

LOVELIEST OF TREES

LOVELIEST of trees, the cherry now
  Is hung with bloom along the bough,
And stands about the woodland ride
Wearing white for Eastertide.

Now, of my threescore years and ten,
Twenty will not come again,
And take from seventy springs a score,
It only leaves me fifty more.

And since to look at things in bloom
Fifty springs are little room,
About the woodlands I will go
To see the cherry hung with snow.

A. E. HOUSMAN

THE BEECH TREE

I'D LIKE to have a garden
  With a beech tree on the lawn;
The little birds that lived there
Would wake me up at dawn.

And in the summer weather
When all the leaves were green,
I'd sit beneath the beech boughs
And see the sky between.

ROSE FYLEMAN

46

DAFFODILS

I WANDERED lonely as a cloud
 That floats on high o'er vales and hills,
When all at once I saw a crowd,
 A host, of golden daffodils;
Beside the lake, beneath the trees,
Fluttering and dancing in the breeze.

Continuous as the stars that shine
 And twinkle on the Milky Way,
They stretched in never-ending line
 Along the margin of a bay:
Ten thousand saw I at a glance,
Tossing their heads in sprightly dance.

The waves beside them danced, but they
 Outdid the sparkling waves in glee:
A poet could not but be gay,
 In such a jocund company:
I gazed—and gazed—but little thought
What wealth the show to me had brought:

For oft, when on my couch I lie
 In vacant or in pensive mood,
They flash upon that inward eye
 Which is the bliss of solitude;
And then my heart with pleasure fills,
And dances with the daffodils.

     WILLIAM WORDSWORTH

SKYLARK AND NIGHTINGALE

WHEN a mounting skylark sings
     In the sunlit summer morn,
I know that heaven is up on high,
     And on earth are fields of corn.

But when a nightingale sings
     In the moonlit summer even,
I know not if earth is merely earth,
     Only that heaven is heaven.

CHRISTINA ROSSETTI

A SUMMER MORNING

I SAW dawn creep across the sky,
   And all the gulls go flying by.
I saw the sea put on its dress
Of blue midsummer loveliness,
And heard the trees begin to stir
Green arms of pine and juniper.
I heard the wind call out and say:
"Get up, my dear, it is today!"

RACHEL FIELD

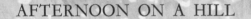

AFTERNOON ON A HILL

I WILL BE the gladdest thing
  Under the sun!
I will touch a hundred flowers
  And not pick one.

I will look at cliffs and clouds
  With quiet eyes,
Watch the wind bow down the grass,
  And the grass rise.

And when lights begin to show
  Up from the town,
I will mark which must be mine,
  And then start down!

                    EDNA ST. VINCENT MILLAY

MAY NIGHT

THE SPRING is fresh and fearless
  And every leaf is new,
The world is brimmed with moonlight,
  The lilac brimmed with dew.

Here in the moving shadows
  I catch my breath and sing—
My heart is fresh and fearless
  And over-brimmed with spring.

                        SARA TEASDALE

THE MOCKING BIRD

THE MOCKING BIRD is the talkingest bird
That ever you'll meet in the month of May.
He teeters and tauters high in the tree,
And he talks all night and he talks all day.
He hardly ever has time to sing
Because of having so much to say.

Sometimes he's fussy and full of worry
(Oh, much too busy to think of a song);
And then it's, "Hurry, now hurry, now hurry!
Ten-thirty, ten-thirty, ten-thirty, ten-thirty!"
Sometimes it's, "Hurry, now hurry, now hurry,
Now hurry, now hurry," the whole day long!

Sometimes he shouts in a rowdy tone,
"Hey, you, come here! Hey, you, come here!"
Sometimes he talks to himself alone,
"Chip-chip . . . chur-r, chur-r . . . chip-chip . . .
    chur-r, chur-r . . ."
And ends with an odd little grating sound,
"Bz-z-z, Bz-z-z!" like an ax on a grinding stone.

And then he'll call, "Potato, potato!"
(Now what is *that* for a bird to sing?)
And then he'll mix them all together:
"Hey, you, come here! Now hurry, now hurry,
Chip-chip, ten-thirty, potato, potato . . ."
And he teeters his tail and he twitches his wing . . .
"Chip-chip, chur-r, chur-r . . . bz-z, bz-z . . ."
A mocking bird is the *talkingest* thing!

A singer, too, as beautiful
As ever you'll hear in the month of May,
Caroling loud from the top of a tree . . .
But he talks all night and he talks all day.
He hardly ever has *time* to sing
Because of having so much to say!

MAURICE LESEMANN

TALENTS DIFFER

"WHAT are you doing there, Robbin a Bobbin,
    Under my window, out in the blue?"
"Building my nest, O Little One, Pretty One,
    Doing the thing that you cannot do!"

"What are you doing now, Robin a Bobbin,
    Under my window, out in the blue?"
"Brooding my eggs, O Little One, Pretty One,
    Doing the thing that you cannot do!"

"What are you doing there, Robin a Bobbin,
    Under my window, out in the blue?"
"Feeding my nestlings, Little One, Pretty One,
    Doing the thing that you cannot do.

"And what are *you* doing, pray, Little One, Pretty One,
    What are you doing, tell me now true?"
"Sewing my patchwork, Robin a Bobbin,
    Doing the thing that *you* cannot do!"

LAURA E. RICHARDS

ROBERT OF LINCOLN

MERRILY swinging on brier and weed,
  Near to the nest of his little dame,
Over the mountain-side or mead,
  Robert of Lincoln is telling his name:
      Bob-o'-link, bob-o'-link,
      Spink, spank, spink;
Snug and safe is that nest of ours,
Hidden among the summer flowers.
                    Chee, chee, chee.

Robert of Lincoln is gayly dressed,
  Wearing a bright black wedding-coat;
White are his shoulders and white his crest.
  Hear him call in his merry note:
      Bob-o'-link, bob-o'-link,
      Spink, spank, spink;
Look, what a nice new coat is mine,
Sure there was never a bird so fine.
                    Chee, chee, chee.

Robert of Lincoln's Quaker wife,
  Pretty and quiet, with plain brown wings,
Passing at home a patient life,
  Broods in the grass while her husband sings:
      Bob-o'-link, bob-o'-link,
      Spink, spank, spink;
Brood, kind creature; you need not fear
Thieves or robbers while I am here.
                    Chee, chee, chee.

52

Six white eggs on a bed of hay,
   Flecked with purple, a pretty sight!
There as the mother sits all day,
   Robert is singing with all his might:
      Bob-o'-link, bob-o'-link,
       Spink, spank, spink;
Nice good wife, that never goes out,
Keeping house while I frolic about.
             Chee, chee, chee.

Soon as the little ones chip the shell,
   Six wide mouths are open for food;
Robert of Lincoln bestirs him well,
   Gathering seeds for the hungry brood.
      Bob-o'-link, bob-o'-link,
       Spink, spank, spink;
This new life is likely to be
Hard for a gay young fellow like me.
             Chee, chee, chee.

Summer wanes; the children are grown;
   Fun and frolic no more he knows;
Robert of Lincoln's a humdrum crone;
   Off he flies, and we sing as he goes:
      Bob-o'-link, bob-o'-link,
       Spink, spank, spink;
When you can pipe that merry old strain,
Robert of Lincoln, come back again.
             Chee, chee, chee.
      WILLIAM CULLEN BRYANT

THE ROMP

THE WIND came dashing from the wood
  With sudden roars and rushes,
Leapfrogging over little hills
  And tagging all the bushes.

It rollicked through the countryside,
  It capered through the town,
It blew one kite into the sky
  And blew another down.

Young Lucy Ann was off to school.
  In vain she whimpered, "Stop!"
It had that girl with skirts a-twirl
  And spinning like a top.

The parson had a tall black hat;
  He tipped it to the people.
Wind caught it as he went along
  And tossed it to a steeple.

Good Mrs. Brown was hanging clothes.
  Calm little frocks and breeches
Began to hop upon the line
  Like frisky imps and witches.

The wind was wild; it couldn't seem
　　To get its fill of fun.
It puffed, "I'm in a perfect gale!"
　　Then roared about the pun.

Skylarking, leaping, on it went,
　　Till old man Weather said,
"There, silly wind, you'll lose your breath.
　　Go home and go to bed."

So, panting hard, it hurried home
　　And weary went to bed.
"What lovely games we had today,
　　The world and I!" it said.

　　　　　　　　NANCY BYRD TURNER

THE PASTURE

I'M going out to clean the pasture spring;
  I'll only stop to rake the leaves away
(And wait to watch the water clear, I may):
I sha'n't be gone long.—You come too.

I'm going out to fetch the little calf
That's standing by the mother. It's so young,
It totters when she licks it with her tongue.
I sha'n't be gone long.—You come too.

ROBERT FROST

THE HAYLOFT

THROUGH all the pleasant meadow-side
  The grass grew shoulder-high,
Till the shining scythes went far and wide
  And cut it down to dry.

Those green and sweetly smelling crops
  They led in wagons home;
And they piled them here in mountain tops
  For mountaineers to roam.

Here is Mount Clear, Mount Rusty-Nail,
  Mount Eagle and Mount High;—
The mice that in these mountains dwell,
  No happier are than I!

Oh, what a joy to clamber there,
  Oh, what a place for play,
With the sweet, the dim, the dusty air,
  The happy hills of hay!

ROBERT LOUIS STEVENSON

ALICE'S SUPPER

FAR down in the meadow the wheat grows green,
And the reapers are whetting their sickles so keen;
And this is the song that I hear them sing,
While cheery and loud their voices ring:
" 'Tis the finest wheat that ever did grow!
And it is for Alice's supper, ho! ho!"

Far down in the valley the old mill stands,
And the miller is rubbing his dusty white hands;
And these are the words of the miller's lay,
As he watches the millstones a-grinding away:
" 'Tis the finest flour that money can buy,
And it is for Alice's supper, hi! hi!"

Downstairs in the kitchen the fire doth glow,
And Maggie is kneading the soft white dough,
And this is the song that she's singing today,
While merry and busy she's working away:
" 'Tis the finest dough by near or by far,
And it is for Alice's supper, ha! ha!"

And now to the nursery comes Nannie at last,
And what in her hand is she bringing so fast?
'Tis a plateful of something all yellow and white,
And she sings as she comes with her smile so bright:
" 'Tis the best bread-and-butter I ever did see!
And it is for Alice's supper, he! he!"

LAURA E. RICHARDS

WHITE BUTTERFLIES

FLY, white butterflies, out to sea,
Frail, pale wings for the wind to try,
Small white wings that we scarce can see,
Fly!

Some fly light as a laugh of glee,
Some fly soft as a long, low sigh;
All to the haven where each would be,
Fly!

ALGERNON CHARLES SWINBURNE

THE CATERPILLAR

BROWN and furry
Caterpillar in a hurry
Take your walk
To the shady leaf, or stalk,
Or what not,
Which may be the chosen spot.
No toad spy you,
Hovering bird of prey pass by you;
Spin and die,
To live again a butterfly.

CHRISTINA ROSSETTI

ARIEL'S SONG

WHERE the bee sucks, there suck I:
    In a cowslip's bell I lie;
There I couch when owls do cry.
On the bat's back I do fly
After summer merrily:
    Merrily, merrily shall I live now
    Under the blossom that hangs on the bough!

WILLIAM SHAKESPEARE

OVER HILL, OVER DALE

OVER hill, over dale,
    Through bush, through brier,
Over park, over pale,
    Through flood, through fire,
I do wander everywhere,
Swifter than the moon's sphere;
And I serve the fairy queen,
To dew her orbs upon the green:
The cowslips tall her pensioners be;
In their gold coats spots you see;
Those be rubies, fairy favors,
In their freckles live their savors:
I must go seek some dewdrops here,
And hang a pearl in every cowslip's ear.

WILLIAM SHAKESPEARE

THE UMBRELLA BRIGADE

"PITTER patter!" falls the rain
    On the schoolroom windowpane.
Such a plashing! such a dashing!
Will it e'er be dry again?
Down the gutter rolls a flood,
And the crossing's deep in mud;
And the puddles! oh, the puddles
Are a sight to stir one's blood!

Chorus.   But let it rain
        Tree-toads and frogs,
        Muskets and pitchforks,
        Kittens and dogs!
        Dash away! plash away!
        Who is afraid?
        Here we go,
        The Umbrella Brigade!

Pull the boots up to the knee!
Tie the hoods on merrily!
Such a hustling! such a jostling!
Out of breath with fun are we.
Clatter, clatter, down the street,
Greeting every one we meet,
With our laughing and our chaffing,
Which the laughing drops repeat.

Chorus.   So let it rain
          Tree-toads and frogs,
          Muskets and pitchforks,
          Kittens and dogs!
          Dash away! plash away!
          Who is afraid?
          Here we go,
          The Umbrella Brigade!

                LAURA E. RICHARDS

THE BROOK

I COME from haunts of coot and hern,
   I make a sudden sally,
And sparkle out among the fern,
   To bicker down a valley.

By thirty hills I hurry down,
   Or slip between the ridges,
By twenty thorps, a little town,
   And half a hundred bridges.

Till last by Philip's farm I flow
   To join the brimming river,
For men may come and men may go,
   But I go on for ever.

I chatter over stony ways,
   In little sharps and trebles,
I bubble into eddying bays,
   I babble on the pebbles.

With many a curve my banks I fret
   By many a field and fallow,
And many a fairy foreland set
   With willow-weed and mallow.

I chatter, chatter, as I flow
   To join the brimming river,
For men may come and men may go,
   But I go on for ever.

I wind about, and in and out,
  With here a blossom sailing,
And here and there a lusty trout,
  And here and there a grayling.

And here and there a foamy flake
  Upon me, as I travel
With many a silvery water-break
  Above the golden gravel,

And draw them all along, and flow
  To join the brimming river,
For men may come and men may go,
  But I go on for ever.

I steal by lawns and grassy plots,
  I slide by hazel covers;
I move the sweet forget-me-nots
  That grow for happy lovers.

I slip, I slide, I gloom, I glance,
  Among the skimming swallows;
I make the netted sunbeam dance
  Against my sandy shallows.

I murmur under moon and stars
  In brambly wildernesses;
I linger by my shingly bars;
  I loiter round my cresses;

And out again I curve and flow
  To join the brimming river,
For men may come and men may go,
  But I go on for ever.

ALFRED TENNYSON

THEME IN YELLOW

I SPOT the hills
With yellow balls in autumn.
I light the prairie cornfields
Orange and tawny gold clusters
And I am called pumpkins.
On the last of October
When dusk is fallen
Children join hands
And circle round me
Singing ghost songs
And love to the harvest moon;
I am a jack-o'-lantern
With terrible teeth
And the children know
I am fooling.

CARL SANDBURG

AUTUMN

THE MORNS are meeker than they were,
The nuts are getting brown;
The berry's cheek is plumper,
The rose is out of town.
The maple wears a gayer scarf,
The field a scarlet gown.
Lest I should be old-fashioned,
I'll put a trinket on.

EMILY DICKINSON

66

FOG

THE fog comes
on little cat feet.

It sits looking
over harbor and city
on silent haunches
and then moves on.
CARL SANDBURG

A VAGABOND SONG

THERE is something in the Autumn
that is native to my blood—
Touch of manner, hint of mood;
And my heart is like a rhyme,
With the yellow and the purple
and the crimson keeping time.

The scarlet of the maples
can shake me like a cry
Of bugles going by.
And my lonely spirit thrills
To see the frosty asters
like smoke upon the hills.

There is something in October
sets the gypsy blood astir,
We must rise and follow her,
When from every hill of flame
She calls and calls each vagabond by name.
BLISS CARMAN

WHEN THE FROST IS ON THE PUNKIN

WHEN the frost is on the punkin and the fodder's
    in the shock,
And you hear the kyouck and gobble of the struttin'
    turkey-cock,
And the clackin' of the guineys, and the cluckin' of the hens,
And the rooster's hallylooyer as he tiptoes on the fence;
O, it's then's the time a feller is a-feelin' at his best,
With the risin' sun to greet him from a night of peaceful rest,
As he leaves the house, bareheaded, and goes out to feed the stock,
When the frost is on the punkin and the fodder's in the shock.

They's something kind o' harty-like about the atmusfere
When the heat of summer's over and the coolin' fall is here—
Of course we miss the flowers, and the blossums on the trees,
And the mumble of the hummin'-birds and buzzin' of the bees;
But the air's so appetizin'; and the landscape through the haze
Of a crisp and sunny morning of the airly autumn days
Is a pictur' that no painter has the colorin' to mock—
When the frost is on the punkin and the fodder's in the shock.

The husky, rusty russel of the tossels of the corn,
And the raspin' of the tangled leaves, as golden as the morn;
The stubble in the furries—kind o' lonesome-like, but still
A-preachin' sermuns to us of the barns they growed to fill;
The strawstack in the medder, and the reaper in the shed;
The hosses in theyr stalls below—the clover overhead!—
O, it sets my hart a-clickin' like the tickin' of a clock,
When the frost is on the punkin and the fodder's in
       the shock!

Then your apples all is gethered, and the ones a feller keeps
Is poured around the cellar-floor in red and yeller heaps;
And your cider-makin's over, and your wimmern-folks
       is through
With theyr mince and apple-butter, and theyr souse and
       sausage, too!
I don't know how to tell it—but ef sich a thing could be
As the Angels wantin' boardin', and they'd call around on *me*—
I'd want to 'commodate 'em—all the whole-indurin' flock—
When the frost is on the punkin and the fodder's in the shock!

JAMES WHITCOMB RILEY

SILVER TREES

IN THE FALL I saw some trees
   With silver leaves, with silver leaves.

From a distance they were quite
As silver as a lake at night.
But closer up I saw that they
Were silver-green and silver-white.

   In the fall I saw some leaves
   On silver trees, on silver trees.

And then I thought, "When they are gone
And snow and ice fall down upon
The branches and the twigs some day,
The trees will *still* have silver on."

AILEEN FISHER

THE FIRST SNOWFALL

THE snow had begun in the gloaming,
   And busily all the night
Had been heaping field and highway
   With a silence deep and white.

Every pine and fir and hemlock
   Wore ermine too dear for an earl,
And the poorest twig on the elm tree
   Was ridged inch deep with pearl.

JAMES RUSSELL LOWELL

LOOK AT THE SNOW!

LOOK at the snow!
   Look at the snow!
Let's all take our sleds,
    And go!
Up the hill we walk slow, slow,
And drag our red sleds in the snow;
But once at the top of the hill, we know
That like the wind they'll go, go, go,
Whizzing down to the flat, below.
Oh, the fun as we swiftly fly
Over the snow like a bird on high!
It takes our breath as our sleds speed by;
No one's as happy as you and I!
—Summers may come, and summers may go,
But *we* like the snow, the snow, the snow!

MARY CAROLYN DAVIES

WHITE FIELDS

IN the wintertime we go
Walking in the fields of snow;

Where there is no grass at all;
Where the top of every wall,

Every fence and every tree,
Is as white as white can be.

Pointing out the way we came,
— Every one of them the same —

All across the fields there be
Prints in silver filigree;

And our mothers always know,
By the footprints in the snow,

Where it is the children go.

JAMES STEPHENS

THE SNOW MAN

ONE DAY the snow man, Sir Benjamin Buzz,
   He started to melt as a snow man does.

Down ran the crown of his icicled hat
Over his forehead and right after that

He noticed his whiskers go lolloping by
Along with his chin and his collar and tie.

Then Benjamin looked and saw that his chest
Was gliding away through his coat and his vest;

And after a little he sighed, "Ho! Hum!
There goes a finger and there goes a thumb!"

And scarce had he spoken when Benjamin felt
That both of his legs were beginning to melt;

Down they ran dribbling, bit after bit,
Like two creamy candles a sunbeam had lit.

"Alas," cried Sir Ben, "I am merely a bump!"
And the next thing he knew he sat down with a thump.

Then little by little he slipped like a sleigh,
And quietly, quietly slithered away;

And next when he noticed the spot he was on,
He looked for himself and he saw he was gone.

And that is the story of Benjamin Buzz,
Who melted one day as a snow man does.

MILDRED PLEW MEIGS

73

FATHER, WE THANK THEE

FOR FLOWERS that bloom about our feet,
  Father, we thank Thee,
For tender grass so fresh and sweet,
  Father, we thank Thee,
For song of bird and hum of bee,
For all things fair we hear or see,
Father in heaven, we thank Thee.

For blue of stream and blue of sky,
  Father, we thank Thee,
For pleasant shade of branches high,
  Father, we thank Thee,
For fragrant air and cooling breeze,
For beauty of the blooming trees,
Father in heaven, we thank Thee.

For this new morning with its light,
  Father, we thank Thee,
For rest and shelter of the night,
  Father, we thank Thee,
For health and food, for love and friends,
For everything Thy goodness sends,
Father in heaven, we thank Thee.

Corinne Dillon

THE PILGRIMS CAME

THE Pilgrims came across the sea,
And never thought of you and me;
And yet it's very strange the way
We think of them Thanksgiving Day.

We tell their story, old and true
Of how they sailed across the blue,
And found a new land to be free
And built their homes quite near the sea.

Every child knows well the tale
Of how they bravely turned the sail,
And journeyed many a day and night,
To worship God as they thought right.

The people think that they were sad,
And grave; I'm sure that they were glad—
They made Thanksgiving Day—that's fun—
We thank the Pilgrims, every one!

ANNETTE WYNNE

A CHRISTMAS FOLK-SONG

THE LITTLE Jesus came to town;
The wind blew up, the wind blew down;
Out in the street the wind was bold;
Now who would house Him from the cold?

Then opened wide a stable door,
Fair were the rushes on the floor;
The Ox put forth a hornèd head;
"Come, little Lord, here make Thy bed."

Uprose the Sheep were folded near:
"Thou Lamb of God, come, enter here."
He entered there to rush and reed,
Who was the Lamb of God indeed.

The little Jesus came to town;
With ox and sheep He laid Him down;
Peace to the byre, peace to the fold,
For that they housed Him from the cold!

LIZETTE WOODWORTH REESE

EVERYWHERE, EVERYWHERE, CHRISTMAS TONIGHT

CHRISTMAS in lands of the fir tree and pine,
  Christmas in lands of the palm tree and vine,
Christmas where snow peaks stand solemn and white,
Christmas where cornfields lie sunny and bright;
  Everywhere, everywhere Christmas tonight!

PHILLIPS BROOKS

THE CHRISTMAS PIE

WITHOUT the door let sorrow lie,
  And if for cold it hap to die,
We'll bury it in a Christmas pie,
  And evermore be merry!

H·H

CHRISTMAS EVE

SEE the pretty snowflakes
    Falling from the sky!
All the trees and houses
    Are like a big cream pie.

Look at all the snowflakes
    As they fill the air:
Look how fast they're falling,
    Do you think Santa'll care?

The snow is falling faster,
    Dear Santa will get wet;
But if I hang my stocking
    I know he won't forget.

J. MORRIS JONES

HILDEGARD
WOODWARD

CHRISTMAS DAY

ON Christmas Day the snow
   Lay soft and thick and white;
But Santa Claus had come
   To see us in the night.

He filled my little stocking —
   I knew he'd not forget;
Oh thank you, thank you, Santa
   Perhaps I'll meet you yet.

You always are so kind to me
   When Christmas Day comes round,
I often wonder how you come!
   You never make a sound.

J. MORRIS JONES

HILDEGARD
WOODWARD

TOMORROW

TOMORROW I'm to get a gift
  (So near to Christmas, too!)
This gift is always fresh and bright
  Yet lasts a whole year through;
It's made in sections, and each day
  I open one, brand new.

Tomorrow I'll begin it: how
  Exciting it will be!
Three hundred sixty-five the times
  A fresh surprise I'll see;
Tomorrow I'm to get a gift —
  A whole New Year — for me!
           DOROTHY BROWN THOMPSON

HUMOROUS POEMS

LAUGHING SONG

COME live and be merry,
  and join with me,
To sing the sweet chorus
  of "Ha, ha, he!"

WILLIAM BLAKE

FUN

I LOVE to see a lobster laugh
Or see a turtle wiggle
Or poke a hippopotamus
And see the monster giggle,
Or even stand around at night
And watch the mountains wriggle.

LEROY F. JACKSON

A FARMER'S BOY

THEY strolled down the lane together,
The sky was studded with stars.
They reached the gate in silence,
And he lifted down the bars.
She neither smiled nor thanked him
Because she knew not how;
For he was just a farmer's boy
And she was a Jersey cow!

82

ELETELEPHONY

ONCE there was an elephant,
   Who tried to use the telephant—
No! no! I mean an elephone
Who tried to use the telephone—
(Dear me! I am not certain quite
That even now I've got it right.)

Howe'er it was, he got his trunk
Entangled in the telephunk;
The more he tried to get it free,
The louder buzzed the telephee—
(I fear I'd better drop the song
Of elephop and telephong!)

LAURA E. RICHARDS

THE DOG
(As Seen by the Cat)

THE DOG is black or white or brown,
  And sometimes spotted like a clown.
He loves to make a foolish noise,
And Human Company enjoys.

The Human People pat his head
And teach him to pretend he's dead,
And beg, and fetch, and carry, too;
Things that no well-bred Cat will do.

At Human jokes, however stale,
He jumps about and wags his tail,
And Human People clap their hands
And think he really understands.

They say "Good Dog" to him. To us
They say "Poor Puss," and make no fuss.
Why Dogs are "good" and Cats are "poor"
I fail to understand, I'm sure.

To Someone very Good and Just,
Who has proved worthy of her trust,
A Cat will *sometimes* condescend —
The Dog is Everybody's friend!

OLIVER HERFORD

84

JACK SIEGEL

THE MYSTERIOUS CAT

I SAW a proud, mysterious cat,
I saw a proud, mysterious cat,
Too proud to catch a mouse or rat —
Mew, mew, mew.

But catnip she would eat, and purr,
But catnip she would eat, and purr.
And goldfish she did much prefer —
Mew, mew, mew.

I saw a cat — 'twas but a dream,
I saw a cat — 'twas but a dream,
Who scorned the slave that brought her cream —
Mew, mew, mew.

Unless the slave were dressed in style,
Unless the slave were dressed in style,
And knelt before her all the while —
Mew, mew, mew.

Did you ever hear of a thing like that?
Did you ever hear of a thing like that?
Did you ever hear of a thing like that?
Oh, what a proud mysterious cat.
Oh, what a proud mysterious cat.
Oh, what a proud mysterious cat.
Mew . . . mew . . . mew.

VACHEL LINDSAY

JACK SIEGEL

THE BUFFALO

THE Buffalo, the Buffalo,
  He had a horrid snuffle, oh!
And not a single Indian chief
Would lend the beast a handkerchief,
Which shows how very, very far
From courtesy some people are.

LAURA E. RICHARDS

THE VULTURE

THE Vulture eats between his meals,
  And that's the reason why
He very, very rarely feels
  As well as you and I.
His eye is dull, his head is bald,
  His neck is growing thinner.
Oh! what a lesson for us all
  To only eat at dinner!

HILAIRE BELLOC

THE YAK

AS A FRIEND to the children commend
me the Yak.
You will find it exactly the thing:
It will carry and fetch, you can ride on its back,
Or lead it about with a string.

The Tartar who dwells on the plains of Tibet
(A desolate region of snow)
Has for centuries made it a nursery pet,
And surely the Tartar should know!

Then tell your papa where the Yak can be got,
And if he is awfully rich
He will buy you the creature — or else he will *not*.
(I cannot be positive which.)

HILAIRE BELLOC

THE PURPLE COW

I NEVER Saw a Purple Cow,
I never Hope to See One;
But I can Tell you, Anyhow,
I'd rather See than Be One.

GELETT BURGESS

THE CAMEL'S HUMP

THE Camel's hump is an ugly lump
Which well you may see at the Zoo;
But uglier yet is the hump we get
From having too little to do.

Kiddies and grown-ups too-oo-oo,
If we haven't enough to do-oo-oo,
    We get the hump —
    Cameelious hump —
The hump that is black and blue!

We climb out of bed with a frouzly head,
    And a snarly-yarly voice.
We shiver and scowl and we grunt and we growl
    At our bath and our boots and our toys;

And there ought to be a corner for me
(And I know there is one for you)
    When we get the hump —
    Cameelious hump —
The hump that is black and blue!

The cure for this ill is not to sit still,
    Or frowst with a book by the fire;
But to take a large hoe and a shovel also,
    And dig till you gently perspire;

88

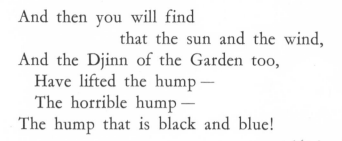

And then you will find
        that the sun and the wind,
And the Djinn of the Garden too,
  Have lifted the hump—
  The horrible hump—
The hump that is black and blue!

I get it as well as you-oo-oo—
If I haven't enough to do-oo-oo!
  We all get hump—
  Cameelious hump—
Kiddies and grown-ups too!

             RUDYARD KIPLING

HOW DOTH THE LITTLE CROCODILE

HOW doth the little crocodile
  Improve his shining tail,
And pour the waters of the Nile
  On every golden scale!

How cheerfully he seems to grin,
  How neatly spreads his claws,
And welcomes little fishes in
  With gently smiling jaws!

             LEWIS CARROLL

HE THOUGHT HE SAW

HE thought he saw a Buffalo
    Upon the chimney-piece:
He looked again, and found it was
    His Sister's Husband's Niece.
"Unless you leave this house!" he said,
    "I'll send for the Police!"

He thought he saw a Rattlesnake
    That questioned him in Greek:
He looked again, and found it was
    The Middle of Next Week.
"The one thing I regret," he said,
    "Is that it cannot speak!"

He thought he saw a Banker's Clerk
    Descending from the bus:
He looked again, and found it was
    A Hippopotamus:
"If this should stay to dine," he said,
    "There won't be much for us!"

90

He thought he saw a Kangaroo
   That worked a coffee-mill:
He looked again, and found it was
   A Vegetable-Pill.
"Were I to swallow this," he said,
   "I should be very ill!"

He thought he saw a Coach-and-Four
   That stood beside his bed:
He looked again, and found it was
   A Bear without a Head.
"Poor thing," he said, "poor silly thing!
   "It's waiting to be fed!"

He thought he saw an Albatross
   That fluttered round the lamp:
He looked again, and found it was
   A Penny-Postage-Stamp.
"You'd best be getting home," he said:
   "The nights are very damp!"

LEWIS CARROLL

JONATHAN BING

POOR old Jonathan Bing
    Went out in his carriage to visit the King,
But everyone pointed and said, "Look at that!
Jonathan Bing has forgotten his hat!"
(He'd forgotten his hat!)

Poor old Jonathan Bing
Went home and put on a new hat for the King,
But by the palace a soldier said, "Hi!
You can't see the King; you've forgotten your tie!"
(He'd forgotten his tie!)

Poor old Jonathan Bing,
He put on a beautiful tie for the King,
But when he arrived, an Archbishop said, "Ho!
You can't come to court in pajamas, you know!"

Poor old Jonathan Bing
Went home and addressed a short note to the King:
"If you please will excuse me, I won't come to tea;
For home's the best place for all people like me!"

BEATRICE CURTIS BROWN

92

A NEW SONG TO SING ABOUT
JONATHAN BING

O JONATHAN BING, O Bingathon Jon
    Forgets where he's going and thinks he has gone.
He wears his false teeth on the top of his head,
And always stands up when he's sleeping in bed.

O Jonathan Bing has a curious way
Of trying to walk into yesterday.
"If I end with my breakfast and start with my tea,
I *ought* to be able to do it," says he.

O Jonathan Bing is a miser, they say,
For he likes to save trouble and put it away.
"If I never get up in the morning," he said,
"I shall save all the trouble of going to bed!"

"O Jonathan Bing! What a way to behave!
And what do you do with the trouble you save?"
"I wrap it up neatly and send it by post
To my friends and relations who need it the most."

BEATRICE CURTIS BROWN

GRANDPA DROPPED HIS GLASSES

GRANDPA dropped his glasses once
In a pot of dye,
And when he put them on again
He saw a purple sky.
Purple fires were rising up
From a purple hill,
Men were grinding purple cider
At a purple mill.
Purple Adeline was playing
With a purple doll;
Little purple dragon flies
Were crawling up the wall.
And at the supper-table
He got crazy as a loon
From eating purple apple dumplings
With a purple spoon.

LEROY F. JACKSON

JOHNNY FIFE AND JOHNNY'S WIFE

OH, JOHNNY FIFE and Johnny's wife,
　To save their toes and heels,
They built themselves a little house
　That ran on rolling wheels.

They hung their parrot at the door
　Upon a painted ring,
And round and round the world they went
　And never missed a thing;

And when they wished to eat they ate,
　And after they had fed,
They crawled beneath a crazy quilt
　And gaily went to bed;

And what they cared to keep they kept,
　And what they both did not,
They poked beneath a picket fence
　And quietly forgot.

Oh, Johnny Fife and Johnny's wife,
　They took their brush and comb,
And round and round the world they went
　And also stayed at home.

MILDRED PLEW MEIGS

TO THE LITTLE GIRL WHO WRIGGLES

DON'T wriggle about any more, my dear!
   I'm sure all your joints must be sore, my dear!
It's wriggle and jiggle, it's twist and it's wiggle,
Like an eel on a shingly shore, my dear,
Like an eel on a shingly shore.

Oh! how do you think you would feel, my dear,
If you should turn into an eel, my dear?
With never an arm to protect you from harm,
And no sign of a toe or a heel, my dear,
No sign of a toe or a heel?

And what do you think you would do, my dear,
Far down in the water so blue, my dear,
Where the prawns and the shrimps, with their curls and
   their crimps,
Would turn up their noses at you, my dear,
Would turn up their noses at you?

The crab he would give you a nip, my dear,
And the lobster would lend you a clip, my dear.
And perhaps if a shark should come by in the dark,
Down his throat you might happen to slip, my dear,
Down his throat you might happen to slip.

Then try to sit still on your chair, my dear!
To your parents 'tis no more than fair, my dear.
For we really don't feel like inviting an eel
Our board and our lodging to share, my dear,
Our board and our lodging to share.

LAURA E. RICHARDS

96

REBECCA,

Who Slammed Doors for Fun and Perished Miserably

A TRICK that everyone abhors
In Little Girls is slamming Doors.
A Wealthy Banker's Little Daughter
Who lived in Palace Green, Bayswater
(By name Rebecca Offendort),
Was given to this Furious Sport.
She would deliberately go
And Slam the door like Billy-Ho!
To make her Uncle Jacob start.
She was not really bad at heart,
But only rather rude and wild:
She was an aggravating child. . . .

It happened that a Marble Bust
Of Abraham was standing just
Above the Door this little Lamb
Had carefully prepared to Slam,
And Down it came! It knocked her flat!
It laid her out! She looked like that.

. . . .

Her Funeral Sermon (which was long
And followed by a Sacred Song)
Mentioned her Virtues, it is true,
But dwelt upon her Vices too,
And showed the Dreadful End of One
Who goes and slams the Door for Fun.

The children who were brought to hear
The awful Tale from far and near
Were much impressed, and inly swore
They never more would slam the Door.
— As often they had done before.

HILAIRE BELLOC

97

LITTLE JOE TUNNEY

THERE was a little boy
    And his name was Joe Tunney.
He had but one failing:
He tried to be funny.

He made himself noticed
In all public places
By making loud noises
And terrible faces.

One day at the circus
He wouldn't sit down.
He stood up and tried
To perform like a clown.

The clown said, "All right,
If you must jump and sing,
Come out with the show
And perform in the ring."

So out ran young Joe,
Acting foolish and wild,
And everyone watched him
But nobody smiled.

The actors all watched him,
The band loudly blared.
In dignified silence
The animals stared.

Thought poor little Joe,
Standing lonely and small,
"Oh, what shall I do?
I'm not funny at all!"

Then the elephant spoke
In the elephant tongue,
"I'll help that boy out —
After all, he's so young."

And he lifted Joe up
With his trunk in the air
And with one mighty sweep
Put him back in his chair.

The people all clapped
And the clowns cheered for Joe,
And he kept very still
For the rest of the show.

REBECCA MCCANN

BENJAMIN JONES GOES SWIMMING

BENJAMIN JONES in confident tones
   Told his wife, "On the Fourth of July
I think I'll compete in the free-for-all meet.
I bet I can win, if I try."

But his wife said, "My word! How very absurd!
You haven't gone swimming for years.
With others so fast, you're sure to be LAST,
And I'll blush to the tips of my ears."

Well, the Fourth quickly came, and waiting acclaim
Were wonderful swimmers galore,
Each poised in his place for the start of the race,
While spectators crowded the shore.

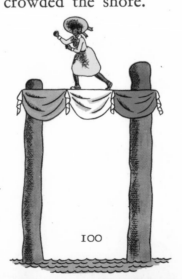

The contest began, and Benjy, poor man,
Was passed on the left and the right.
His pace was so slow that a crab saw his toe
And thought it would venture a bite.

Ben noticed the crab as it started to grab
And — perhaps the result can be guessed:
The thought of his toe in the claws of his foe
Made him swim like a swimmer possessed!

And the crowd on the shore sent up a great roar
As Ben took the lead in the dash,
While his wife on the dock received such a shock
She fell in the lake with a splash.

AILEEN FISHER

A NONSENSE RHYME

RINGLETY-jing!
    And what will we sing?
Some little crinkety-crankety thing
    That rhymes and chimes,
    And skips, sometimes,
As though wound up with a kink in the spring.

    Grunkety-krung!
    And chunkety-plung!
Sing the song that the bullfrog sung,—
    A song of the soul
    Of a mad tadpole
That met his fate in a leaky bowl:
And it's O for the first false wiggle he made
In a sea of pale pink lemonade!
    And it's O for the thirst
    Within him pent,
    And the hopes that burst
    As his reason went —
When his strong arm failed and his strength was spent!

    Sing, O sing
    Of the things that cling,
And the claws that clutch and the fangs that sting —
    Till the tadpole's tongue
    And his tail upflung
Quavered and failed with a song unsung!

O the dank despair in the rank morass,
Where the crawfish crouch in the cringing grass,
And the long limp rune of the loon wails on
　For the mad, sad soul
　Of a bad tadpole
Forever lost and gone!

　　Jinglety-jee!
　And now we'll see
What the last of the lay shall be,
　As the dismal tip of the tune, O friends,
　Swoons away and the long tale ends.
　　And it's O and alack!
　For the tangled legs
　　And the spangled back
　Of the green grig's eggs,
　　And the unstrung strain
　　Of the strange refrain
That the winds wind up like a strand of rain!

　　And it's O,
　　　Also,
　For the ears wreathed low,
Like a laurel wreath on the lifted brow
Of the frog that chants of the why and how,
　And the wherefore too, and the thus and so
　Of the wail he weaves in a woof of woe!
Twangle, then, with your wrangling strings,
The tinkling links of a thousand things!
And clang the pang of a maddening moan
Till the Echo, hid in a land unknown,
　Shall leap as he hears, and hoot and hoo
　Like the wretched wraith of a Whoopty-Doo!
　　　　　　　JAMES WHITCOMB RILEY

THE ORGAN GRINDERS' GARDEN

IN the winter, in the winter,
   When the clouds shake snow,
I know a little garden
   Where the organ grinders go;

   A cozy little garden
      Where the fountain makes a fizz,
   And round about the lattices
      The sunbeams sizz;

         Where underneath the bushes
            In the nodding afternoons,
         The frisky little organs sit
            And spill their tinky tunes;

   While tingle, tingle, tangle,
      Go the pennies in the cup,
   As all the baby monkeys
      Practice picking pennies up.

   In the winter, in the winter,
      When the sharp winds blow,
   I know a little garden
      Where the organ grinders go;

A giddy little garden
  Where the fruit is always ripe,
And every grinding grinder
  Sits and pulls upon a pipe;

While all the father monkeys
  Hang their fezzes on the twigs,
And teach the baby monkeys
  How to master little jigs;

Until at last the mothers come,
  As day begins to fade,
And tuck the baby monkeys up
  To snoozle in the shade.

In the winter, in the winter,
  When the clouds shake snow,
I know a little garden
  Where the organ grinders go;

A garden where the grinders
  And the monkeys on a string,
Are pleased to wait serenely
  For the coming of the spring.

MILDRED PLEW MEIGS

FATHER WILLIAM

"YOU are old, Father William," the young man said,
  "And your hair has become very white;
And yet you incessantly stand on your head—
  Do you think, at your age, it is right?"

"In my youth," Father William replied to his son,
  "I feared it might injure the brain;
But, now that I'm perfectly sure I have none,
  Why, I do it again and again."

"You are old," said the youth, "as I mentioned before,
  And have grown most uncommonly fat;
Yet you turned a back-somersault in at the door—
  Pray, what is the reason of that?"

"In my youth," said the sage, as he shook his grey locks,
  "I kept all my limbs very supple
By the use of this ointment—one shilling the box—
  Allow me to sell you a couple?"

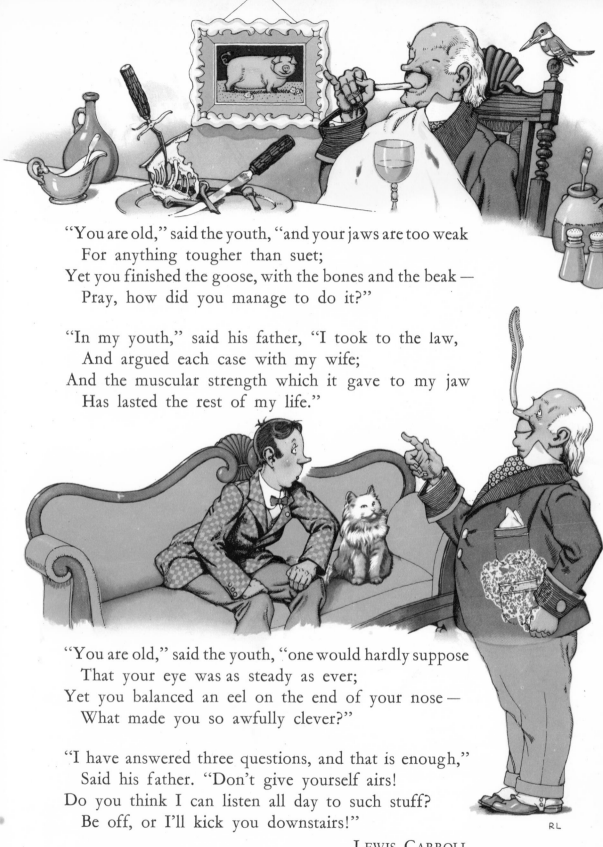

"You are old," said the youth, "and your jaws are too weak
　　For anything tougher than suet;
Yet you finished the goose, with the bones and the beak —
　　Pray, how did you manage to do it?"

"In my youth," said his father, "I took to the law,
　　And argued each case with my wife;
And the muscular strength which it gave to my jaw
　　Has lasted the rest of my life."

"You are old," said the youth, "one would hardly suppose
　　That your eye was as steady as ever;
Yet you balanced an eel on the end of your nose —
　　What made you so awfully clever?"

"I have answered three questions, and that is enough,"
　　Said his father. "Don't give yourself airs!
Do you think I can listen all day to such stuff?
　　Be off, or I'll kick you downstairs!"

LEWIS CARROLL

THE MAGNANIMOUS SUN

The Sun
  Rises.
The Sun
  Sets.
The Sun sees a lot
  He
Kindly
  Forgets!

VACHEL LINDSAY

THE MAN IN THE MOON

THE MAN in the Moon
  as he sails the sky
Is a very remarkable skipper.
But he made a mistake
When he tried to take
A drink of milk from the Dipper.
He dipped right into the Milky Way
And slowly and carefully filled it.
The Big Bear growled
And the Little Bear howled,
And frightened him so he spilled it.

STORYTELLING POEMS AND BALLADS

PIRATE STORY

THREE of us afloat in the meadow by the swing,
    Three of us aboard in the basket on the lea.
Winds are in the air, they are blowing in the spring,
    And waves are on the meadow like the waves there
        are at sea.

Where shall we adventure, today that we're afloat,
    Wary of the weather and steering by a star?
Shall it be to Africa, a-steering of the boat,
    To Providence, or Babylon, or off to Malabar?

ROBERT LOUIS STEVENSON

THE POTATOES' DANCE
(A Poem Game)

Down cellar," said the cricket,
  "Down cellar," said the cricket,
"Down cellar," said the cricket,
"I saw a ball last night,

In honor of a lady,
In honor of a lady,
In honor of a lady,
Whose wings were pearly white.

The breath of bitter weather,
The breath of bitter weather,
The breath of bitter weather,
Had smashed the cellar pane.

We entertained a drift of leaves,
We entertained a drift of leaves,
We entertained a drift of leaves,
And then of snow and rain.

But we were dressed for winter,
But we were dressed for winter,
But we were dressed for winter,
And loved to hear it blow

In honor of the lady,
In honor of the lady,
In honor of the lady,
Who makes potatoes grow,

Our guest the Irish lady,
The tiny Irish lady,
The airy Irish lady,
Who makes potatoes grow.

"Potatoes were the waiters,
Potatoes were the waiters,
Potatoes were the waiters,
Potatoes were the band,
Potatoes were the dancers
Kicking up the sand,
Kicking up the sand,
Kicking up the sand,
Potatoes were the dancers
Kicking up the sand.
Their legs were old burnt matches,
Their legs were old burnt matches,
Their legs were old burnt matches,
Their arms were just the same.
They jigged and whirled and scrambled,
Jigged and whirled and scrambled,
Jigged and whirled and scrambled,
In honor of the dame,
The noble Irish lady
Who makes potatoes dance,

S. A.

The witty Irish lady,
The saucy Irish lady,
The laughing Irish lady
Who makes potatoes prance.

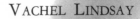

"There was just one sweet potato.
He was golden brown and slim.
The lady loved his dancing,
The lady loved his dancing,
The lady loved his dancing,
She danced all night with him,
She danced all night with him.
Alas, he wasn't Irish.
So when she flew away,
They threw him in the coalbin,
And there he is today,
Where they cannot hear his sighs
And his weeping for the lady,
The glorious Irish lady,
The beauteous Irish lady,
Who
Gives
Potatoes
Eyes."

VACHEL LINDSAY

A BUNNY ROMANCE

THE Bunnies are a feeble folk,
  Whose weakness is their strength;
To shun a gun a Bun will run
To almost any length.

Now once, when war's alarms were rife
In the ancestral wood
Where the kingdom of the Bunnies
For centuries had stood,
The king, for fear long peace had made
His subjects overbold,
To wake the glorious spirit
Of timidity of old,
Announced one day he would bestow
Princess Bunita's hand
On the Bunny who should prove himself
Most timid in the land.

Next day a proclamation
Was posted in the wood:
"To the Flower of Timidity,
The Pick of Bunnyhood:
His Majesty the Bunny king
Commands you to appear
At a tournament—at such a date
In such and such a year—
Where his Majesty will then bestow
Princess Bunita's hand
On the Bunny who will prove himself
Most timid in the land."

Then every timid Bunny's heart
Swelled with exultant fright
At the thought of doughty deeds of fear
And prodigies of flight.
For the motto of the Bunnies,
As perhaps you are aware,
Is, "Only the faint-hearted
Are deserving of the fair."

They fell at once to practicing,
These Bunnies, one and all,
Till some could almost die of fright
To hear a petal fall.
And one enterprising Bunny
Got up a special class
To teach the art of fainting
At your shadow on the grass.

At length—at length—at length
The moment is at hand!
And trembling all from head to foot
A hundred Bunnies stand.
And a hundred Bunny mothers
With anxiety turn gray
Lest their offspring dear should lose their fear
And linger in the fray.

Never before in Bunny lore
Was such a stirring sight
As when the bugle sounded
To begin the glorious flight!
A hundred Bunnies, like a flash,
All disappeared from sight
Like arrows from a hundred bows,
None swerved to left or right—
Some north, some south, some east, some west—
And none of them, 'tis plain,
Till he has gone around the earth
Will e'er be seen again.

It may be in a hundred weeks,
Perchance a hundred years—
Whenever it may be, 'tis plain
The one who first appears
Is the one who ran the fastest;
He wins the Princess' hand,
And gains the glorious title of
"Most Timid in the Land."

OLIVER HERFORD

115

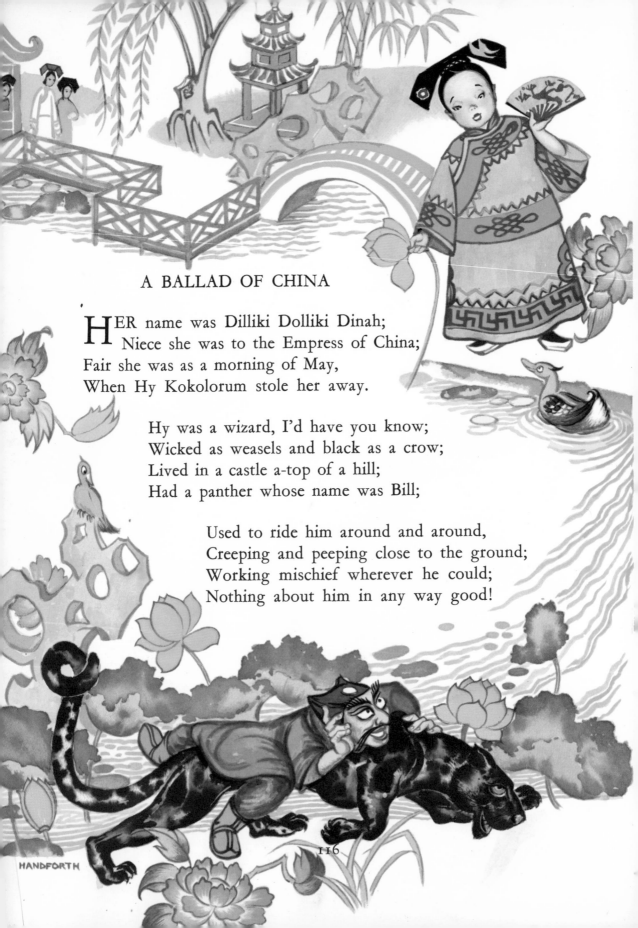

A BALLAD OF CHINA

HER name was Dilliki Dolliki Dinah;
Niece she was to the Empress of China;
Fair she was as a morning of May,
When Hy Kokolorum stole her away.

Hy was a wizard, I'd have you know;
Wicked as weasels and black as a crow;
Lived in a castle a-top of a hill;
Had a panther whose name was Bill;

Used to ride him around and around,
Creeping and peeping close to the ground;
Working mischief wherever he could;
Nothing about him in any way good!

HANDFORTH

Saw the maiden one midsummer morn,
(Sweetest creature that ever was born!),
Creeped and peeped in his wizardly way,
Catched her and snatched her and stole her away!

All through China arose a cry:
"Some one has stolen our Dilliki Di!"
People gathered in every forum,
Crying, "It must be Hy Kokolorum!"

All the Barons in China land,
Ling the lofty and Bing the bland,
Kong the kingly and Bong the brave,
Vowed a vow to find and save

Darling Dilliki Dolliki Dinah
(Niece, you know, to the Empress of China;
Fair, you know, as a morning in May),
Whom Hy Kokolorum had stolen away.

Now in a kingly, ringly row,
Round and about the Hill they go,
Ling the lofty and Bing the bland,
Kong and Bong, and there they stand,

Weaving a weird and spinning a spell,
All with intent to quash and quell
Hy Kokolorum, worker of woe,
Wicked as weasels and black as a crow.

Dilliki Dinah was weeping her fill,
When stepped up softly the panther Bill;
Whispered, "If you will give me a kiss,
I'll turn your sorrow to bubbling bliss!"

She, to animals always kind,
Said, "No! Really? Well, I don't mind!"
Dropped a kiss on his nose so pink,
And—goodness gracious! what *do* you think?

He turned to a beautiful Golden King,
Crown and sceptre and everything!
Ran the old wizard through and through,
Saying, "Now there is an end of *you!*"

Caught the maiden up in his arms,
Broke through the net of spells and charms,
Cried to the Barons bold and brave,
"*I've* had the honor to find and save

Darling Dilliki Dolliki Dinah,
Niece (I learn) to the Empress of China,
Fair (I swear) as a morning of May,
And she is my Queen from this very day!"

LAURA E. RICHARDS

A TRAGIC STORY

THERE lived a sage in days of yore,
 And he a handsome pigtail wore;
But wondered much and sorrowed more,
 Because it hung behind him.

He mused upon this curious case,
And swore he'd change the pigtail's place,
And have it hanging at his face,
 Not dangling there behind him.

Says he, "The mystery I've found—
Says he, "The mystery I've found!
I'll turn me round,"—he turned him round;
 But still it hung behind him.

Then round and round, and out and in,
All day the puzzled sage did spin;
In vain—it mattered not a pin—
 The pigtail hung behind him.

And right and left and round about,
And up and down and in and out
He turned; but still the pigtail stout
 Hung steadily behind him.

And though his efforts never slack,
And though he twist, and twirl, and tack,
Alas! still faithful to his back,
 The pigtail hangs behind him.

WILLIAM MAKEPEACE THACKERAY

ANTONIO

ANTONIO, Antonio,
  Was tired of living alonio.
    He thought he would woo
    Miss Lissamy Lu,
Miss Lissamy Lucy Molonio.

  Antonio, Antonio,
  Rode off on his polo-ponio.
    He found the fair maid
    In a bowery shade,
  A-sitting and knitting alonio.

    Antonio, Antonio,
    Said, "If you will be my ownio,
      I'll love you true,
      And I'll buy for you
    An icery creamery conio!"

      "Oh, *nonio*, Antonio!
      You're far too bleak and bonio!
        And all that I wish,
        You singular fish,
      Is that you will quickly begonio."

        Antonio, Antonio,
        He uttered a dismal moanio;
          Then he ran off and hid
          (Or I'm told that he did)
        In the Antecatarctical Zonio.

LAURA E. RICHARDS

121

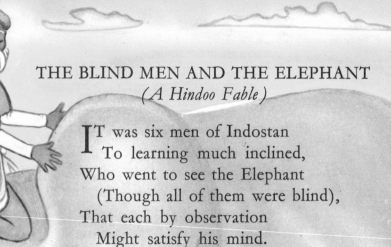

THE BLIND MEN AND THE ELEPHANT
(A Hindoo Fable)

IT was six men of Indostan
  To learning much inclined,
Who went to see the Elephant
  (Though all of them were blind),
That each by observation
  Might satisfy his mind.

The *First* approached the Elephant,
  And happening to fall
Against his broad and sturdy side,
  At once began to bawl:
"God bless me! but the Elephant
  Is very like a wall!"

The *Second*, feeling of the tusk,
  Cried, "Ho! what have we here
So very round and smooth and sharp?
  To me 'tis mighty clear
This wonder of an Elephant
  Is very like a spear!"

The *Third* approached the animal,
  And happening to take
The squirming trunk within his hands,
  Thus boldly up and spake:
"I see," quoth he, "the Elephant
  Is very like a snake!"

The *Fourth* reached out an eager hand,
  And felt about the knee.
"What most this wondrous beast is like
  Is mighty plain," quoth he;
" 'Tis clear enough the Elephant
  Is very like a tree!"

The *Fifth,* who chanced to touch the ear,
 Said: "E'en the blindest man
Can tell what this resembles most;
 Deny the fact who can,
This marvel of an Elephant
 Is very like a fan!"

The *Sixth* no sooner had begun
 About the beast to grope,
Than, seizing on the swinging tail
 That fell within his scope,
"I see," quoth he, "the Elephant
 Is very like a rope!"

And so these men of Indostan
 Disputed loud and long,
Each in his own opinion
 Exceeding stiff and strong,
Though each was partly in the right
 And all were in the wrong!

MORAL

So oft in theologic wars,
 The disputants, I ween,
Rail on in utter ignorance
 Of what each other mean,
And prate about an Elephant
 Not one of them has seen!

JOHN GODFREY SAXE

D'AULAIRE.

THE MOUNTAIN AND THE SQUIRREL

(A Fable)

THE mountain and the squirrel
Had a quarrel,
And the former called the latter "Little prig";
Bun replied,
"You are doubtless very big;
But all sorts of things and weather
Must be taken in together,
To make up a year
And a sphere.
And I think it no disgrace
To occupy my place.
If I'm not so large as you,
You are not so small as I,
And not half so spry.
I'll not deny you make
A very pretty squirrel track;
Talents differ; all is well and wisely put;
If I cannot carry forests on my back,
Neither can you crack a nut."

RALPH WALDO EMERSON

SING ME A SONG

SING me a song of a lad that is gone,
  Say, could that lad be I?
Merry of soul he sailed on a day
  Over the sea to Skye.

Mull was astern, Rum on the port,
  Egg on the starboard bow;
Glory of youth glowed in his soul:
  Where is that glory now?

Sing me a song of a lad that is gone,
  Say, could that lad be I?
Merry of soul he sailed on a day
  Over the sea to Skye.

Give me again all that was there,
  Give me the sun that shone!
Give me the eyes, give me the soul,
  Give me the lad that's gone!

Sing me a song of a lad that is gone,
  Say, could that lad be I?
Merry of soul he sailed on a day
  Over the sea to Skye.

Billow and breeze, islands and seas,
  Mountains of rain and sun,
All that was good, all that was fair,
  All that was me is gone.

ROBERT LOUIS STEVENSON

THE PIED PIPER OF HAMELIN

HAMELIN TOWN'S in Brunswick,
  By famous Hanover city;
The river Weser, deep and wide,
Washes its wall on the southern side;
A pleasanter spot you never spied;
But, when begins my ditty,
  Almost five hundred years ago,
  To see the townsfolk suffer so
From vermin, was a pity.

  Rats!
They fought the dogs and killed the cats,
  And bit the babies in the cradles,
And ate the cheeses out of the vats,
  And licked the soup from the cooks' own ladles,
Split open the kegs of salted sprats,
Made nests inside men's Sunday hats,
And even spoiled the women's chats
  By drowning their speaking
  With shrieking and squeaking
In fifty different sharps and flats.

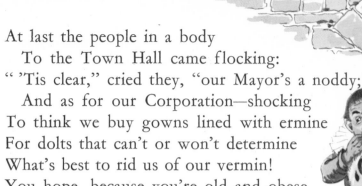

At last the people in a body
  To the Town Hall came flocking:
" 'Tis clear," cried they, "our Mayor's a noddy;
  And as for our Corporation—shocking
To think we buy gowns lined with ermine
For dolts that can't or won't determine
What's best to rid us of our vermin!
You hope, because you're old and obese,
To find in the furry civic robe ease?
Rouse up, sirs! Give your brains a racking
To find the remedy we're lacking,
Or, sure as fate, we'll send you packing!"
At this the Mayor and Corporation
Quaked with a mighty consternation.

An hour they sat in council;
  At length the Mayor broke silence:
"For a guilder I'd my ermine gown sell,
  I wish I were a mile hence!
It's easy to bid one rack one's brain—
I'm sure my poor head aches again,
I've scratched it so, and all in vain.
Oh for a trap, a trap, a trap!"
Just as he said this, what should hap
At the chamber-door but a gentle tap?
"Bless us," cried the Mayor, "what's that?"
(With the Corporation as he sat,
Looking little though wondrous fat;
Nor brighter was his eye, nor moister
Than a too-long-opened oyster,
Save when at noon his paunch grew mutinous
For a plate of turtle green and glutinous.)
"Only a scraping of shoes on the mat?
Anything like the sound of a rat
Makes my heart go pit-a-pat!"

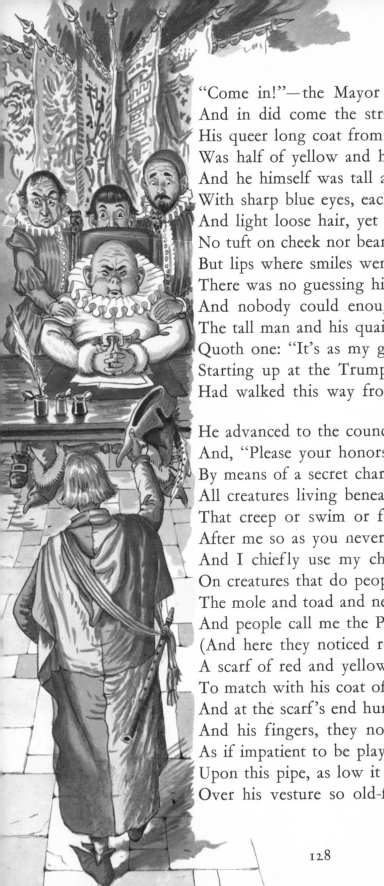

"Come in!"—the Mayor cried, looking bigger:
And in did come the strangest figure!
His queer long coat from heel to head
Was half of yellow and half of red,
And he himself was tall and thin,
With sharp blue eyes, each like a pin,
And light loose hair, yet swarthy skin,
No tuft on cheek nor beard on chin,
But lips where smiles went out and in;
There was no guessing his kith and kin:
And nobody could enough admire
The tall man and his quaint attire.
Quoth one: "It's as my great-grandsire,
Starting up at the Trump of Doom's tone,
Had walked this way from his painted tombstone!"

He advanced to the council-table:
And, "Please your honors," said he, "I'm able,
By means of a secret charm, to draw
All creatures living beneath the sun,
That creep or swim or fly or run,
After me so as you never saw!
And I chiefly use my charm
On creatures that do people harm,
The mole and toad and newt and viper;
And people call me the Pied Piper."
(And here they noticed round his neck
A scarf of red and yellow stripe,
To match with his coat of the self-same check;
And at the scarf's end hung a pipe;
And his fingers, they noticed, were ever straying
As if impatient to be playing
Upon this pipe, as low it dangled
Over his vesture so old-fangled.)

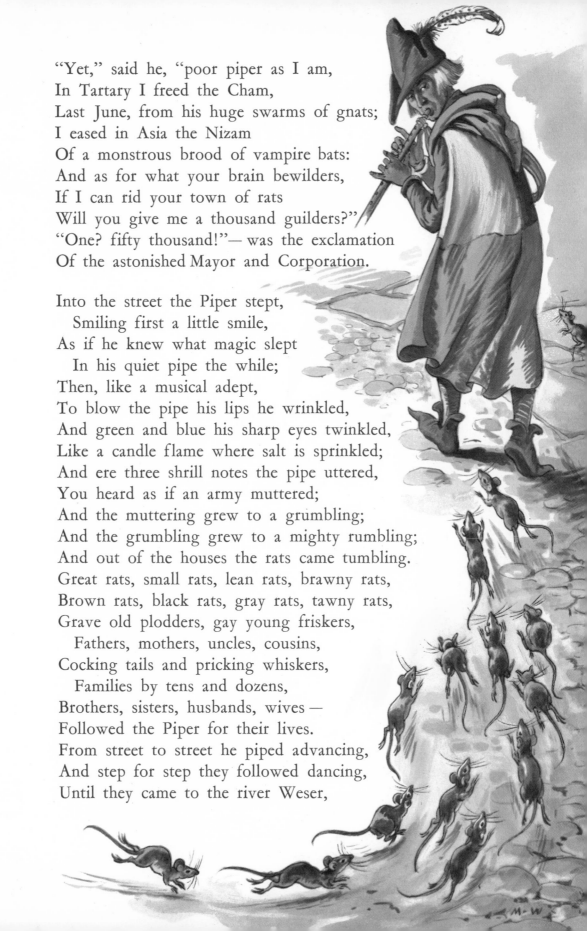

"Yet," said he, "poor piper as I am,
In Tartary I freed the Cham,
Last June, from his huge swarms of gnats;
I eased in Asia the Nizam
Of a monstrous brood of vampire bats:
And as for what your brain bewilders,
If I can rid your town of rats
Will you give me a thousand guilders?"
"One? fifty thousand!"— was the exclamation
Of the astonished Mayor and Corporation.

Into the street the Piper stept,
  Smiling first a little smile,
As if he knew what magic slept
  In his quiet pipe the while;
Then, like a musical adept,
To blow the pipe his lips he wrinkled,
And green and blue his sharp eyes twinkled,
Like a candle flame where salt is sprinkled;
And ere three shrill notes the pipe uttered,
You heard as if an army muttered;
And the muttering grew to a grumbling;
And the grumbling grew to a mighty rumbling;
And out of the houses the rats came tumbling.
Great rats, small rats, lean rats, brawny rats,
Brown rats, black rats, gray rats, tawny rats,
Grave old plodders, gay young friskers,
  Fathers, mothers, uncles, cousins,
Cocking tails and pricking whiskers,
  Families by tens and dozens,
Brothers, sisters, husbands, wives —
Followed the Piper for their lives.
From street to street he piped advancing,
And step for step they followed dancing,
Until they came to the river Weser,

Wherein all plunged and perished!
—Save one who, stout as Julius Caesar,
Swam across and lived to carry
(As he, the manuscript he cherished)
To Rat-land home his commentary:
Which was, "At the first shrill notes of the pipe,
I heard a sound as of scraping tripe,
And putting apples, wondrous ripe,
Into a cider-press's gripe:
And a moving away of pickle-tub boards,
And a leaving ajar of conserve-cupboards,
And a drawing the corks of train-oil flasks,
And a breaking the hoops of butter-casks:
And it seemed as if a voice
(Sweeter far than by harp or by psaltery
Is breathed) called out, 'Oh rats, rejoice!
The world is grown to one vast drysaltery!
So munch on, crunch on, take your nuncheon,
Breakfast, supper, dinner, luncheon!'
And just as a bulky sugar-puncheon,
All ready staved, like a great sun shone
Glorious scarce an inch before me,
Just as methought it said, 'Come, bore me!'
—I found the Weser rolling o'er me."

You should have heard the Hamelin people
Ringing the bells till they rocked the steeple.
"Go," cried the Mayor, "and get long poles,
Poke out the nests and block up the holes!
Consult with carpenters and builders,
And leave in our town not even a trace
Of the rats!"—when suddenly, up the face
Of the Piper perked in the market-place,
With a, "First, if you please, my thousand guilders!"

A thousand guilders! The Mayor looked blue;
So did the Corporation too.
For council dinners made rare havoc
With Claret, Moselle, Vin-de-Grave, Hock;
And half the money would replenish
Their cellar's biggest butt with Rhenish.
To pay this sum to a wandering fellow
With a gypsy coat of red and yellow!
"Beside," quoth the Mayor with a knowing wink,
"Our business was done at the river's brink;
We saw with our eyes the vermin sink,
And what's dead can't come to life, I think.
So, friend, we're not the folks to shrink
From the duty of giving you something for drink,
And a matter of money to put in your poke;
But as for the guilders, what we spoke
Of them, as you very well know, was in joke.
Beside, our losses have made us thrifty.
A thousand guilders! Come, take fifty!"

The Piper's face fell, and he cried,
"No trifling! I can't wait, beside!
I've promised to visit by dinnertime
Bagdat, and accept the prime
Of the Head Cook's pottage, all he's rich in,

For having left, in the Caliph's kitchen,
Of a nest of scorpions no survivor:
With him I proved no bargain-driver,
With you, don't think I'll bate a stiver!
And folks who put me in a passion
May find me pipe after another fashion."

"How?" cried the Mayor, "d'ye think I brook
Being worse treated than a Cook?
Insulted by a lazy ribald
With idle pipe and vesture piebald?
You threaten us, fellow? Do your worst,
Blow your pipe there till you burst!"

Once more he stept into the street,
   And to his lips again
   Laid his long pipe of smooth straight cane;
And ere he blew three notes (such sweet
Soft notes as yet musician's cunning
Never gave the enraptured air)
There was a rustling that seemed like a bustling
Of merry crowds justling at pitching and hustling;
Small feet were pattering, wooden shoes clattering,
Little hands clapping and little tongues chattering,
And, like fowls in a farmyard when barley is scattering,
Out came the children running.
All the little boys and girls,
With rosy cheeks and flaxen curls,
And sparkling eyes and teeth like pearls,
Tripping and skipping, ran merrily after
The wonderful music with shouting and laughter.

The Mayor was dumb, and the Council stood
As if they were changed into blocks of wood,
Unable to move a step, or cry
To the children merrily skipping by,

— Could only follow with the eye
That joyous crowd at the Piper's back.
But how the Mayor was on the rack,
And the wretched Council's bosoms beat,
As the Piper turned from the High Street
To where the Weser rolled its waters
Right in the way of their sons and daughters!
However, he turned from South to West,
And to Koppelberg Hill his steps addressed,
And after him the children pressed;
Great was the joy in every breast.
"He never can cross that mighty top!
He's forced to let the piping drop,
And we shall see our children stop!"
When, lo, as they reached the mountainside,
A wondrous portal opened wide,
As if a cavern was suddenly hollowed;
And the Piper advanced and the children followed,
And when all were in to the very last,
The door in the mountainside shut fast.
Did I say, all? No! One was lame,
And could not dance the whole of the way;
And in after years, if you would blame
His sadness, he was used to say,—
"It's dull in our town since my playmates left!
I can't forget that I'm bereft
Of all the pleasant sights they see,
Which the Piper also promised me.
For he led us, he said, to a joyous land,
Joining the town and just at hand,
Where waters gushed and fruit-trees grew
And flowers put forth a fairer hue,
And everything was strange and new;
The sparrows were brighter than peacocks here
And their dogs outran our fallow deer,
And honeybees had lost their stings,

And horses were born with eagles' wings:
And just as I became assured
My lame foot would be speedily cured,
The music stopped and I stood still,
And found myself outside the hill,
Left alone against my will,
To go now limping as before,
And never hear of that country more!"

Alas, alas for Hamelin!
　There came into many a burgher's pate
　A text which says that heaven's gate
　Opes to the rich at as easy rate
As the needle's eye takes a camel in!
The Mayor sent East, West, North, and South
To offer the Piper, by word of mouth,
　Wherever it was men's lot to find him,
Silver and gold to his heart's content,
If he'd only return the way he went,
　And bring the children behind him.
But when they saw 'twas a lost endeavor,
And Piper and dancers were gone forever,
They made a decree that lawyers never

Should think their records dated duly
If, after the day of the month and year,
These words did not as well appear,
"And so long after what happened here
  On the Twenty-second of July,
Thirteen hundred and seventy-six:"
And the better in memory to fix
The place of the children's last retreat,
They called it, the Pied Piper's Street—
Where any one playing on pipe or tabor
Was sure for the future to lose his labor.
Nor suffered they hostelry or tavern

  To shock with mirth a street so solemn;
But opposite the place of the cavern
  They wrote the story on a column,
And on the great church-window painted
The same, to make the world acquainted
How their children were stolen away,
And there it stands to this very day.
And I must not omit to say
That in Transylvania there's a tribe
Of alien people who ascribe
The outlandish ways and dress
On which their neighbors lay such stress,
To their fathers and mothers having risen
Out of some subterraneous prison
Into which they were trepanned
Long time ago in a mighty band
Out of Hamelin town in Brunswick land,
But how or why, they don't understand.

So, Willy, let me and you be wipers
Of scores out with all men—especially pipers!
And, whether they pipe us free from rats or from mice,
If we've promised them aught, let us keep our promise!

                                ROBERT BROWNING

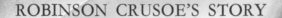

ROBINSON CRUSOE'S STORY

THE night was thick and hazy
  When the "Piccadilly Daisy"
Carried down the crew and captain in the sea;
  And I think the water drowned 'em,
  For they never, never found 'em,
And I know they didn't come ashore with me.

  Oh! 'twas very sad and lonely
  When I found myself the only
Population of this cultivated shore;
  But I've made a little tavern
  In a rocky little cavern,
And I sit and watch for people at the door.

  I spent no time in looking
  For a girl to do my cooking,
As I'm quite a clever hand at making stews;
  But I had that fellow Friday
  Just to keep the tavern tidy,
And to put a Sunday polish on my shoes.

  I have a little garden
  That I'm cultivating lard in,
And the things I eat are rather tough and dry;
  For I live on toasted lizards,
  Prickly pears, and parrot gizzards,
And I'm really very fond of beetle-pie.

  The clothes I had were furry,
  And it made me fret and worry
When I found the moths were eating off the hair;
  And I had to scrape and sand 'em,
  And I boiled 'em and I tanned 'em,
Till I got the fine morocco suit I wear.

Nino Carbe

I sometimes seek diversion
In a family excursion
With the few domestic animals you see;
And we take along a carrot
As refreshment for the parrot,
And a little can of jungleberry tea.

Then we gather, as we travel,
Bits of moss and dirty gravel,
And we chip off little specimens of stone;
And we carry home as prizes
Funny bugs, of handy sizes,
Just to give the day a scientific tone.

If the roads are wet and muddy
We remain at home and study,—
For the Goat is very clever at a sum,—
And the Dog, instead of fighting,
Studies ornamental writing,
While the Cat is taking lessons on the drum.

We retire at eleven,
And we rise again at seven;
And I wish to call attention, as I close,
To the fact that all the scholars
Are correct about their collars,
And particular in turning out their toes.

CHARLES E. CARRYL

137

PIRATE DON DURK OF DOWDEE

HO, FOR the Pirate Don Durk of Dowdee!
　　He was as wicked as wicked could be,
But oh, he was perfectly gorgeous to see!
　　The Pirate Don Durk of Dowdee.

His conscience, of course, was as black as a bat,
But he had a floppety plume on his hat
And when he went walking it jiggled — like that!
　　The plume of the Pirate Dowdee.

His coat it was handsome and cut with a slash,
And often as ever he twirled his mustache
Deep down in the ocean the mermaids went splash,
　　Because of Don Durk of Dowdee.

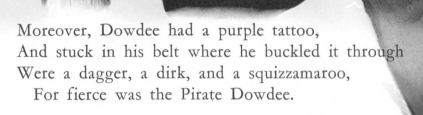

Moreover, Dowdee had a purple tattoo,
And stuck in his belt where he buckled it through
Were a dagger, a dirk, and a squizzamaroo,
   For fierce was the Pirate Dowdee.

So fearful he was he would shoot at a puff,
And always at sea when the weather grew rough
He drank from a bottle and wrote on his cuff,
   Did Pirate Don Durk of Dowdee.

Oh, he had a cutlass that swung at his thigh
And he had a parrot called Pepperkin Pye,
And a zigzaggy scar at the end of his eye
   Had Pirate Don Durk of Dowdee.

He kept in a cavern, this buccaneer bold,
A curious chest that was covered with mould,
And all of his pockets were jingly with gold!
   Oh jing! went the gold of Dowdee.

His conscience, of course, it was crook'd like a squash,
But both of his boots made a slickery slosh,
And he went through the world with a wonderful swash,
   Did Pirate Don Durk of Dowdee.

It's true he was wicked as wicked could be,
His sins they outnumbered a hundred and three,
But oh, he was perfectly gorgeous to see,
   The Pirate Don Durk of Dowdee.

MILDRED PLEW MEIGS

THE MILLER OF THE DEE

THERE dwelt a miller, hale and bold,
    Beside the River Dee;
He worked and sang from morn till night,
    No lark more blithe than he;
And this the burden of his song
    Forever used to be:
"I envy no man, no, not I,
    And no one envies me!"

"Thou'rt wrong, my friend!" said old King Hal,
  "As wrong as wrong can be;
For could my heart be light as thine,
  I'd gladly change with thee.
And tell me now what makes thee sing
  With voice so loud and free,
While I am sad, though I'm the King,
  Beside the River Dee?"

The miller smiled and doffed his cap;
  "I earn my bread," quoth he;
"I love my wife, I love my friend,
  I love my children three.
I owe no one I cannot pay,
  I thank the River Dee
That turns the mill that grinds the corn
  To feed my babes and me."

"Good friend," said Hal, and sighed the while,
  "Farewell! and happy be;
But say no more, if thou'dst be true,
  That no one envies thee.
Thy mealy cap is worth my crown;
  Thy mill my kingdom's fee!
Such men as thou are England's boast,
  Oh, miller of the Dee!"

CHARLES MACKAY

THE RAGGEDY MAN

O THE Raggedy Man! He works fer Pa;
  An' he's the goodest man ever you saw!
He comes to our house every day,
An' waters the horses, an' feeds 'em hay;
An' he opens the shed — an' we all ist laugh
When he drives out our little old wobble-ly calf;
An' nen — ef our hired girl says he can —
He milks the cow fer 'Lizabuth Ann.—
  Ain't he a' awful good Raggedy Man?
  Raggedy! Raggedy! Raggedy Man!

Why, the Raggedy Man — he's ist so good
He splits the kindlin' an' chops the wood;
An' nen he spades in our garden, too,
An' does most things 'at *boys* can't do! —
He clumbed clean up in our big tree
An' shooked a' apple down fer me —
An' nother'n', too, fer 'Lizabuth Ann —
An' nother'n', too, fer the Raggedy Man.—
  Ain't he a' awful kind Raggedy Man?
  Raggedy! Raggedy! Raggedy Man!

An' the Raggedy Man, he knows most rhymes
An' tells 'em, ef I be good, sometimes:
Knows 'bout Giunts, an' Griffuns, an' Elves,
An' the Squidgicum-Squees 'at swallers therselves!
An' wite by the pump in our pasture-lot,
He showed me the hole 'at the Wunks is got,
'At lives 'way deep in the ground, an' can
Turn into me, er 'Lizabuth Ann!
Er Ma, er Pa, er the Raggedy Man!
    Ain't he a funny old Raggedy Man?
        Raggedy! Raggedy! Raggedy Man!

The Raggedy Man — one time when he
Was makin' a little bow-'n'-arry fer me,
Says, "When *you're* big like your Pa is,
Air you go' to keep a fine store like his —
An' be a rich merchunt — an' wear fine clothes? —
Er what *air* you go' to be, goodness knows!"
An' nen he laughed at 'Lizabuth Ann,
An' I says, "'M go' to be a Raggedy Man! —
    I'm ist go' to be a nice Raggedy Man!"
        Raggedy! Raggedy! Raggedy Man!

JAMES WHITCOMB RILEY

THE WIND AND THE MOON

Said the Wind to the Moon, "I will blow you out!
    You stare
    In the air
    As if crying Beware,
Always looking what I am about:
I hate to be watched; I will blow you out!"

The Wind blew hard, and out went the Moon.
    So deep
    On a heap
    Of clouds, to sleep
Down lay the Wind, and slumbered soon,
Muttering low, "I've done for that Moon!"

He turned in his bed: she was there again!
    On high
    In the sky
    With her one ghost-eye,
The Moon shone white and alive and plain:
Said the Wind, "I will blow you out again!"

The Wind blew hard, and the Moon grew slim.
    "With my sledge
    And my wedge
    I have knocked off her edge!
I will blow," said the wind, "right fierce and grim,
The creature will soon be slimmer than slim!"

He blew and he blew, and she thinned to a thread.
    "One puff
    More's enough
    To blow her to snuff!
One good puff more where the last was bred,
And glimmer, glimmer, glum will go that thread!"

He blew a great blast, and the thread was gone.
    In the air
    Nowhere
    Was a moonbeam bare;
Larger and nearer the shy stars shone:
    Sure and certain the Moon was gone!

The Wind he took to his revels once more;
    On down,
    And in town,
    A merry-mad clown,
He leaped and halloed with whistle and roar —
When there was that glimmering thread once more!

He flew in a rage — he danced and blew;
    But in vain
    Was the pain
    Of his bursting brain,
For still the Moon-scrap the broader grew
The more he swelled his big cheeks and blew.

MARJORIE
TUCKER

Slowly she grew — till she filled the night,
    And shone
    On her throne
    In the sky alone
A matchless, wonderful, silvery light,
Radiant and lovely, the queen of the night.

Said the Wind, "What a marvel of power am I!
    With my breath,
    In good faith,
    I blew her to death! —
First blew her away right out of the sky,
Then blew her in: what a strength am I!"

But the Moon she knew nought of the silly affair;
    For, high
    In the sky
    With her one white eye,
Motionless miles above the air,
She never had heard the great Wind blare.

GEORGE MacDONALD

JEST 'FORE CHRISTMAS

FATHER calls me William,
   sister calls me Will,
Mother calls me Willie,
   but the fellers call me Bill!
Mighty glad I ain't a girl —
   ruther be a boy,
Without them sashes, curls, an' things
   that's worn by Fauntleroy!
Love to chawnk green apples
   an' go swimmin' in the lake —
Hate to take the castor-ile
   they give for belly-ache!
'Most all the time, the whole year round,
   there ain't no flies on me,
But jest 'fore Christmas
   I'm as good as I kin be!

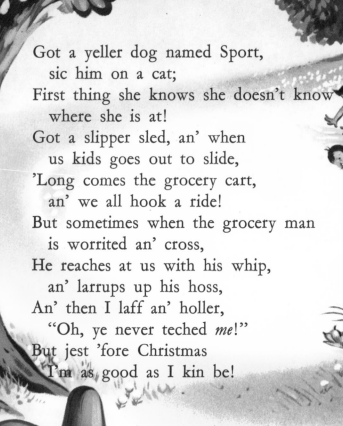

Got a yeller dog named Sport,
    sic him on a cat;
First thing she knows she doesn't know
    where she is at!
Got a slipper sled, an' when
    us kids goes out to slide,
'Long comes the grocery cart,
    an' we all hook a ride!
But sometimes when the grocery man
    is worrited an' cross,
He reaches at us with his whip,
    an' larrups up his hoss,
An' then I laff an' holler,
    "Oh, ye never teched *me*!"
But jest 'fore Christmas
    I'm as good as I kin be!

Gran'ma says she hopes that
    when I git to be a man,
I'll be a missionarer like
    her oldest brother, Dan,
As was et up by cannibuls
    that lives in Ceylon's Isle,
Where every prospect pleases,
    an' only man is vile!
But gran'ma she has never been
    to see a Wild West show,
Nor read the Life of Daniel Boone,
    or else I guess she'd know
That Buff'lo Bill an' cowboys
    is good enough for me!
Excep' jest 'fore Christmas,
    when I'm good as I kin be!

And then old Sport he hangs around,
  so solemn-like an' still,
His eyes they keep a-sayin':
  "What's the matter, little Bill?"
The old cat sneaks down off her perch
  an' wonders what's become
Of them two enemies of hern
  that used to make things hum!
But I am so perlite an' tend
  so earnestly to biz,
That Mother says to Father:
  "How improved our Willie is!"
But Father, havin' been a boy
  hisself, suspicions me
When, jest 'fore Christmas,
  I'm as good as I kin be!

For Christmas, with its lots an' lots
  of candies, cakes, an' toys,
Was made, they say, for proper kids,
  an' not for naughty boys;
So wash yer face an' bresh yer haid,
  an' mind yer p's and q's,
An' don't bust out yer pantaloons,
  and don't wear out yer shoes;
Say "Yessum" to the ladies,
  an' "Yessur" to the men,
An' when they's company,
  don't pass yer plate for pie again;
But, thinkin' of the things yer'd like
  to see upon that tree,
Jest 'fore Christmas
  be as good as yer kin be!

EUGENE FIELD

A VISIT FROM ST. NICHOLAS

TWAS the night before Christmas, when all through the house
Not a creature was stirring, not even a mouse;
The stockings were hung by the chimney with care,
In hopes that St. Nicholas soon would be there;
The children were nestled all snug in their beds,
While visions of sugar-plums danced in their heads;
And mamma in her 'kerchief, and I in my cap,
Had just settled our brains for a long winter's nap,
When out on the lawn there arose such a clatter,
I sprang from the bed to see what was the matter.
Away to the window I flew like a flash,
Tore open the shutters and threw up the sash.
The moon on the breast of the new-fallen snow
Gave the luster of mid-day to objects below,
When, what to my wondering eyes should appear,
But a miniature sleigh, and eight tiny reindeer,
With a little old driver, so lively and quick,
I knew in a moment it must be St. Nick.
More rapid than eagles his coursers they came,
And he whistled, and shouted, and called them by name:
"Now, *Dasher!* now, *Dancer!* now, *Prancer* and *Vixen!*
On, *Comet!* on, *Cupid!* on, *Donder* and *Blitzen!*
To the top of the porch! to the top of the wall!
Now dash away! dash away! dash away all!"
As dry leaves that before the wild hurricane fly,
When they meet with an obstacle, mount to the sky,
So up to the house-top the coursers they flew,
With the sleigh full of toys, and St. Nicholas too.

And then, in a twinkling, I heard on the roof
The prancing and pawing of each little hoof.
As I drew in my head, and was turning around,
Down the chimney St. Nicholas came with a bound.
He was dressed all in fur, from his head to his foot,
And his clothes were all tarnished with ashes and soot;
A bundle of toys he had flung on his back,
And he looked like a peddler just opening his pack.
His eyes — how they twinkled! his dimples how merry!
His cheeks were like roses, his nose like a cherry!
His droll little mouth was drawn up like a bow,
And the beard of his chin was as white as the snow;
The stump of a pipe he held tight in his teeth,
And the smoke it encircled his head like a wreath;
He had a broad face and a little round belly,
That shook, when he laughed, like a bowlful of jelly.
He was chubby and plump, a right jolly old elf,
And I laughed when I saw him, in spite of myself;
A wink of his eye and a twist of his head,
Soon gave me to know I had nothing to dread;
He spoke not a word, but went straight to his work,
And filled all the stockings; then turned with a jerk,
And laying his finger aside of his nose,
And giving a nod, up the chimney he rose;
He sprang to his sleigh, to his team gave a whistle,
And away they all flew like the down of a thistle.
But I heard him exclaim, ere he drove out of sight,
"Happy Christmas to all, and to all a good-night."

CLEMENT CLARKE MOORE

151

THE DIVERTING HISTORY OF JOHN GILPIN

JOHN GILPIN was a citizen
  Of credit and renown,
A trainband captain eke was he
  Of famous London town.

John Gilpin's spouse said to her dear,
  "Though wedded we have been
These twice ten tedious years, yet we
  No holiday have seen.

"Tomorrow is our wedding day,
  And we will then repair
Unto the Bell at Edmonton
  All in a chaise and pair.

"My sister, and my sister's child,
  Myself, and children three,
Will fill the chaise; so you must ride
  On horseback after we."

He soon replied, "I do admire
  Of womankind but one,
And you are she, my dearest dear;
  Therefore it shall be done.

"I am a linendraper bold,
  As all the world doth know,
And my good friend the calender
  Will lend his horse to go."

Quoth Mrs. Gilpin, "That's well said;
    And, for that wine is dear,
We will be furnished with our own,
    Which is both bright and clear."

John Gilpin kissed his loving wife;
    O'erjoyed was he to find
That, though on pleasure she was bent,
    She had a frugal mind.

The morning came, the chaise was brought,
    But yet was not allowed
To drive up to the door, lest all
    Should say that she was proud.

So three doors off the chaise was stayed,
    Where they did all get in;
Six precious souls, and all agog
    To dash through thick and thin!

Smack went the whip,
        round went the wheels,
    Were never folk so glad;
The stones did rattle underneath,
    As if Cheapside were mad.

John Gilpin at his horse's side
    Seized fast the flowing mane,
And up he got, in haste to ride,
    But soon came down again;

For saddletree scarce reached had he
    His journey to begin,
When, turning round his head, he saw
    Three customers come in.

So down he came; for loss of time,
    Although it grieved him sore,
Yet loss of pence, full well he knew,
    Would trouble him much more.

'Twas long before the customers
    Were suited to their mind,
When Betty screaming came downstairs,
    "The wine is left behind!"

"Good lack!" quoth he —"yet bring it me,
    My leathern belt likewise,
In which I bear my trusty sword
    When I do exercise."

Now Mistress Gilpin (careful soul!)
    Had two stone bottles found,
To hold the liquor that she loved,
    And keep it safe and sound.

Each bottle had a curling ear,
    Through which the belt he drew,
And hung a bottle on each side,
    To make his balance true.

Then, over all, that he might be
    Equipped from top to toe,
His long red cloak, well brushed and neat,
    He manfully did throw.

Now see him mounted once again
   Upon his nimble steed,
Full slowly pacing o'er the stones,
   With caution and good heed!

But, finding soon a smoother road
   Beneath his well-shod feet,
The snorting beast began to trot,
   Which galled him in his seat.

So, "Fair and softly," John he cried,
   But John he cried in vain;
That trot became a gallop soon,
   In spite of curb and rein.

So stooping down, as needs he must
   Who cannot sit upright,
He grasped the mane with both his hands,
   And eke with all his might.

His horse, who never in that sort
   Had handled been before,
What thing upon his back had got
   Did wonder more and more.

Away went Gilpin, neck or nought;
   Away went hat and wig!
He little dreamt, when he set out,
   Of running such a rig!

The wind did blow, the cloak did fly,
   Like streamer long and gay,
Till, loop and button failing both,
   At last it flew away.

Then might all people well discern
  The bottles he had slung;
A bottle swinging at each side,
  As hath been said or sung.

The dogs did bark, the children screamed,
  Up flew the windows all;
And every soul cried out,"Well done!"
  As loud as he could bawl.

Away went Gilpin — who but he?
  His fame soon spread around —
"He carries weight! he rides a race!
  'Tis for a thousand pound!"

And still, as fast as he drew near,
  'Twas wonderful to view
How in a trice the turnpike men
  Their gates wide open threw.

And now, as he went bowing down
  His reeking head full low,
The bottles twain behind his back
  Were shattered at a blow.

Down ran the wine into the road,
  Most piteous to be seen,
Which made his horse's flanks to smoke
  As they had basted been.

But still he seemed to carry weight,
  With leathern girdle braced;
For all might see the bottle-necks
  Still dangling at his waist.

Thus all through merry Islington
   These gambols he did play,
And till he came unto the Wash
   Of Edmonton so gay.

And there he threw the wash about
   On both sides of the way,
Just like unto a trundling mop,
   Or a wild goose at play.

At Edmonton his loving wife
   From the balcony espied
Her tender husband, wondering much
   To see how he did ride.

"Stop, stop, John Gilpin! Here's the house!"
   They all at once did cry;
"The dinner waits and we are tired."
   Said Gilpin, "So am I!"

But yet his horse was not a whit
   Inclined to tarry there;
For why? his owner had a house
   Full ten miles off, at Ware.

So like an arrow swift he flew,
   Shot by an archer strong;
So did he fly — which brings me to
   The middle of my song.

Away went Gilpin, out of breath,
   And sore against his will,
Till at his friend the calender's
   His horse at last stood still.

The calender, amazed to see
  His neighbor in such trim,
Laid down his pipe, flew to the gate,
  And thus accosted him:

"What news? what news? your tidings tell;
  Tell me you must and shall.
Say why bareheaded you are come,
  Or why you come at all?"

Now Gilpin had a pleasant wit,
  And loved a timely joke;
And thus unto the calender
  In merry guise he spoke;

"I came because your horse would come;
  And, if I well forbode,
My hat and wig will soon be here —
  They are upon the road."

The calender, right glad to find
  His friend in merry pin,
Returned him not a single word,
  But to the house went in;

Whence straight he came with hat and wig
  A wig that flowed behind,
A hat not much the worse for wear,
  Each comely in its kind.

He held them up, and, in his turn
  Thus showed his ready wit:
"My head is twice as big as yours,
  They therefore needs must fit.

"But let me scrape the dirt away
　　That hangs upon your face;
And stop and eat, for well you may
　　Be in a hungry case."

Said John, "It is my wedding day,
　　And all the world would stare,
If wife should dine at Edmonton,
　　And I should dine at Ware!"

So, turning to his horse, he said,
　　"I am in haste to dine;
'Twas for your pleasure you came here,
　　You shall go back for mine."

Ah, luckless speech, and bootless boast!
　　For which he paid full dear;
For, while he spake, a braying ass
　　Did sing most loud and clear;

Whereat his horse did snort, as he
　　Had heard a lion roar,
And galloped off with all his might,
　　As he had done before.

Away went Gilpin, and away
　　Went Gilpin's hat and wig!
He lost them sooner than at first.
　　For why? — they were too big!

Now Mistress Gilpin, when she saw
　　Her husband posting down
Into the country far away,
　　She pulled out half-a-crown;

And thus unto the youth she said,
  That drove them to the Bell,
"This shall be yours, when you bring back
  My husband safe and well."

The youth did ride, and soon did meet
  John coming back amain;
Whom in a trice he tried to stop,
  By catching at his rein.

But, not performing what he meant,
  And gladly would have done,
The frighted steed he frighted more,
  And made him faster run.

Away went Gilpin, and away
  Went postboy at his heels,
The postboy's horse right glad to miss
  The lumbering of the wheels.

Six gentlemen upon the road,
  Thus seeing Gilpin fly,
With postboy scampering in the rear,
  They raised the hue and cry:

"Stop thief! stop thief! a highwayman!"
  Not one of them was mute;
And all and each that passed that way
  Did join in the pursuit.

And now the turnpike gates again
  Flew open in short space,
The tollmen thinking as before,
  That Gilpin rode a race.

And so he did, and won it too,
  For he got first to town,
Nor stopped till where he had got up
  He did again get down.

Now let us sing, "Long live the king,
  And Gilpin, long live he";
And when he next doth ride abroad,
  May I be there to see!

              WILLIAM COWPER

THE HIGHWAYMAN

Part One

THE WIND was a torrent of darkness
  among the gusty trees,
The moon was a ghostly galleon
  tossed upon cloudy seas,
The road was a ribbon of moonlight
  over the purple moor,
And the highwayman came riding —
    Riding — riding —
The highwayman came riding,
  up to the old inn-door.

He'd a French cocked-hat on his forehead,
  a bunch of lace at his chin,
A coat of the claret velvet,
  and breeches of brown doe-skin;
They fitted with never a wrinkle:
  his boots were up to the thigh!
And he rode with a jeweled twinkle,
    His pistol butts a-twinkle,
His rapier hilt a-twinkle,
  under the jeweled sky.

Over the cobbles he clattered
  and clashed in the dark inn-yard,
And he tapped with his whip on the shutters,
  but all was locked and barred;
He whistled a tune to the window,
  and who should be waiting there
But the landlord's black-eyed daughter,
    Bess, the landlord's daughter,
Plaiting a dark red love-knot
  into her long black hair.

Maud and Miska Petersham

And dark in the dark old inn-yard
  a stable-wicket creaked
Where Tim the ostler listened;
  his face was white and peaked;
His eyes were hollows of madness,
  his hair like moldy hay,
But he loved the landlord's daughter,
    The landlord's red-lipped daughter,
Dumb as a dog he listened,
  and he heard the robber say —

"One kiss, my bonny sweetheart,
  I'm after a prize to-night,
But I shall be back with the yellow gold
  before the morning light;
Yet, if they press me sharply,
  and harry me through the day,
Then look for me by moonlight,
    Watch for me by moonlight,
I'll come to thee by moonlight,
  though hell should bar the way."

He rose upright in the stirrups;
  he scarce could reach her hand,
But she loosened her hair i' the casement!
  His face burnt like a brand
As the black cascade of perfume
  came tumbling over his breast;
And he kissed its waves in the moonlight,
    (Oh, sweet black waves in the moonlight!)
Then he tugged at his rein in the moonlight,
  and galloped away to the West.

Part Two

He did not come in the dawning;
  he did not come at noon;
And out o' the tawny sunset,
  before the rise o' the moon,
When the road was a gypsy's ribbon,
  looping the purple moor,
A red-coat troop came marching —
    Marching — marching —
King George's men came marching
  up to the old inn-door.

They said no word to the landlord,
  they drank his ale instead,
But they gagged his daughter and bound her
  to the foot of her narrow bed;
Two of them knelt at her casement,
  with muskets at their side!
There was death at every window;
    And hell at one dark window;
For Bess could see, through her casement,
  the road that *he* would ride.

They had tied her up to attention,
  with many a sniggering jest;
They had bound a musket beside her,
  with the barrel beneath her breast!
"Now keep good watch!" and they kissed her.
  She heard the dead man say —
Look for me by moonlight;
  Watch for me by moonlight;
I'll come to thee by moonlight,
  though hell should bar the way!

She twisted her hands behind her;
   but all the knots held good!
She writhed her hands till her fingers
   were wet with sweat or blood!
They stretched and strained in the darkness,
   and the hours crawled by like years,
Till, now, on the stroke of midnight,
    Cold, on the stroke of midnight,
The tip of one finger touched it!
   The trigger at least was hers!

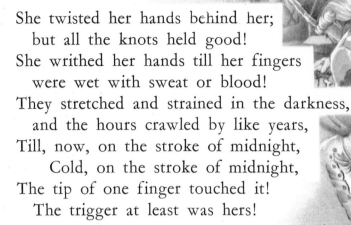

The tip of one finger touched it;
   she strove no more for the rest!
Up, she stood to attention,
   with the barrel beneath her breast,
She would not risk their hearing;
   she would not strive again;
For the road lay bare in the moonlight;
    Blank and bare in the moonlight;
And the blood of her veins in the moonlight
   throbbed to her love's refrain.

Tlot-tlot; tlot-tlot! Had they heard it?
   The horse-hoofs ringing clear;
Tlot-tlot, tlot-tlot, in the distance?
   Were they deaf that they did not hear?
Down the ribbon of moonlight,
   over the brow of the hill,
The highwayman came riding,
    Riding, riding!
The red-coats looked to their priming!
   She stood up, straight and still!

The Petershams

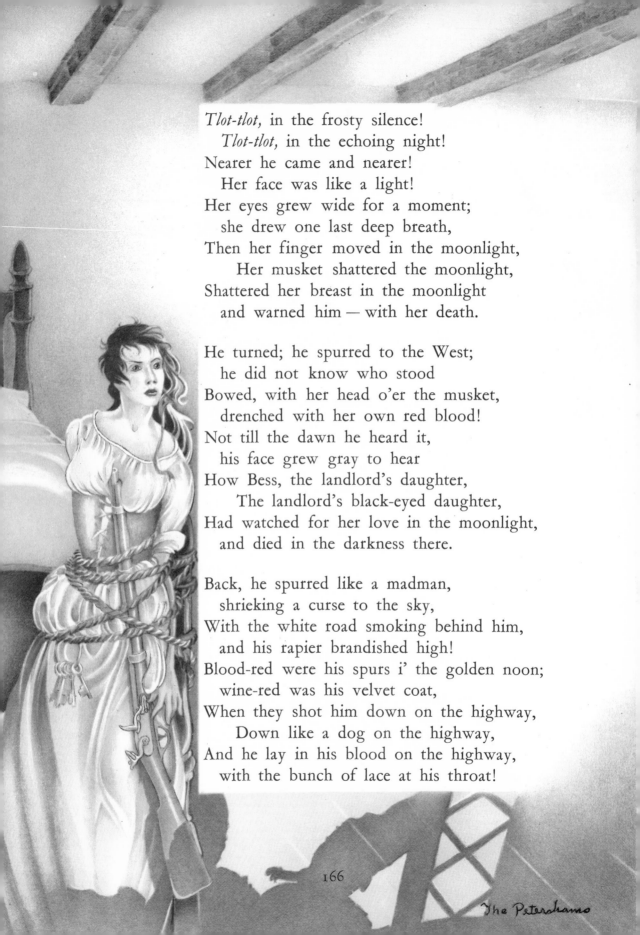

Tlot-tlot, in the frosty silence!
   Tlot-tlot, in the echoing night!
Nearer he came and nearer!
   Her face was like a light!
Her eyes grew wide for a moment;
   she drew one last deep breath,
Then her finger moved in the moonlight,
    Her musket shattered the moonlight,
Shattered her breast in the moonlight
   and warned him — with her death.

He turned; he spurred to the West;
   he did not know who stood
Bowed, with her head o'er the musket,
   drenched with her own red blood!
Not till the dawn he heard it,
   his face grew gray to hear
How Bess, the landlord's daughter,
   The landlord's black-eyed daughter,
Had watched for her love in the moonlight,
   and died in the darkness there.

Back, he spurred like a madman,
   shrieking a curse to the sky,
With the white road smoking behind him,
   and his rapier brandished high!
Blood-red were his spurs i' the golden noon;
   wine-red was his velvet coat,
When they shot him down on the highway,
   Down like a dog on the highway,
And he lay in his blood on the highway,
   with the bunch of lace at his throat!

The Petershams

And still of a winter's night, they say,
    when the wind is in the trees,
When the moon is a ghostly galleon
    tossed upon cloudy seas,
When the road is a ribbon of moonlight
    over the purple moor,
A highwayman comes riding—
      Riding—riding—
A highwayman comes riding,
    up to the old inn-door.

Over the cobbles he clatters
    and clangs in the dark inn-yard;
And he taps with his whip on the shutters,
    but all is locked and barred;
He whistles a tune to the window,
    and who should be waiting there
But the landlord's black-eyed daughter,
    Bess, the landlord's daughter,
Plaiting a dark red love-knot
    into her long black hair.

ALFRED NOYES

Ilse Bischoff

THE RIDDLING KNIGHT

THERE were three sisters fair and bright,
Jennifer, Gentle, and Rosemary,

And they three loved one valiant knight —
  As the dow flies over the mulberry-tree.

The eldest sister let him in,
And barr'd the door with a silver pin.

The second sister made his bed,
And placed soft pillows under his head.

The youngest sister that same night
Was resolved for to wed wi' this valiant knight.

'And if you can answer questions three,
O then, fair maid, I'll marry wi' thee.

'O what is louder nor a horn,
Or what is sharper nor a thorn?

'Or what is heavier nor the lead,
Or what is better nor the bread?

'Or what is longer nor the way,
Or what is deeper nor the sea?'—

'O shame is louder nor a horn,
And hunger is sharper nor a thorn.

'O sin is heavier nor the lead,
The blessing's better nor the bread.

'O the wind is longer nor the way
And love is deeper nor the sea.'

'You have answer'd aright my questions three,
    Jennifer, Gentle, and Rosemary;

And now, fair maid, I'll marry wi' thee,
    As the dow flies over the mulberry-tree.'

J. Bischoff

LADY CLARE

IT was the time when lilies blow,
  And clouds are highest up in air,
Lord Ronald brought a lily-white doe
  To give his cousin, Lady Clare.

I trow they did not part in scorn;
  Lovers long betrothed were they;
They two will wed the morrow morn —
  God's blessing on the day!

"He does not love me for my birth,
  Nor for my lands so broad and fair;
He loves me for my own true worth,
  And that is well," said Lady Clare.

In there came old Alice the nurse,
  Said, "Who was this that went from thee?"
"It was my cousin," said Lady Clare;
  "Tomorrow he weds with me."

"O God be thanked," said Alice the nurse,
  "That all comes round so just and fair!
Lord Ronald is heir of all your lands,
  And you are *not* the Lady Clare."

"Are ye out of your mind, my nurse, my nurse,"
    Said Lady Clare, "that ye speak so wild?"
"As God's above," said Alice the nurse,
    "I speak the truth: you are my child.

"The old earl's daughter died at my breast;
    I speak the truth, as I live by bread!
I buried her like my own sweet child,
    And put my child in her stead."

"Falsely, falsely have ye done,
    O mother," she said, "if this be true,
To keep the best man under the sun
    So many years from his due."

"Nay now, my child," said Alice the nurse,
    "But keep the secret for your life,
And all you have will be Lord Ronald's,
    When you are man and wife."

"If I'm a beggar born," she said,
    "I will speak out, for I dare not lie.
Pull off, pull off, the brooch of gold,
    And fling the diamond necklace by."

"Nay now, my child," said Alice the nurse,
    "But keep the secret all ye can."
She said, "Not so; but I will know
    If there be any faith in man."

"Nay now, what faith?" said Alice the nurse,
  "The man will cleave unto his right."
"And he shall have it," the lady replied,
  "Though I should die tonight."

"Yet give one kiss to your mother dear!
  Alas, my child, I sinned for thee!"
"O mother, mother, mother," she said,
  "So strange it seems to me.

"Yet here's a kiss for my mother dear,
  My mother dear, if this be so,
And lay your hand upon my head,
  And bless me, mother, ere I go."

She clad herself in a russet gown,
  She was no longer Lady Clare;
She went by dale, and she went by down,
  With a single rose in her hair.

The lily-white doe Lord Ronald had brought
  Leaped up from where she lay,
Dropped her head in the maiden's hand,
  And followed her all the way.

Down stepped Lord Ronald from his tower:
  "O Lady Clare, you shame your worth!
Why come you dressed like a village maid,
  That are the flower of the earth?"

"If I come dressed like a village maid,
  I am but as my fortunes are;
I am a beggar born," she said,
  "And not the Lady Clare."

"Play me no tricks," said Lord Ronald,
  "For I am yours in word and in deed.
Play me no tricks," said Lord Ronald,
  "Your riddle is hard to read."

O, and proudly stood she up!
  Her heart within her did not fail;
She looked into Lord Ronald's eyes,
  And told him all her nurse's tale.

He laughed a laugh of merry scorn;
  He turned and kissed her where she stood;
"If you are not the heiress born,
  And I," said he, "the next in blood,

"If you are not the heiress born,
  And I," said he, "the lawful heir,
We two will wed tomorrow morn,
  And you shall still be Lady Clare."

                              ALFRED TENNYSON

HIAWATHA'S CHILDHOOD

BY the shores of Gitche Gumee,
By the shining Big Sea-Water,
Stood the wigwam of Nokomis,
Daughter of the Moon, Nokomis.
Dark behind it rose the forest,
Rose the black and gloomy pine trees,
Rose the firs with cones upon them;
Bright before it beat the water,
Beat the clear and sunny water,
Beat the shining Big Sea-Water.

There the wrinkled old Nokomis
Nursed the little Hiawatha,
Rocked him in his linden cradle,
Bedded soft in moss and rushes,
Safely bound with reindeer sinews;
Stilled his fretful wail by saying,
"Hush! the Naked Bear will hear thee!"
Lulled him into slumber, singing,
"Ewa-yea! my little owlet!
Who is this that lights the wigwam?
With his great eyes lights the wigwam?
Ewa-yea! my little owlet!"

Many things Nokomis taught him
Of the stars that shine in heaven;
Showed him Ishkoodah, the comet,
Ishkoodah, with fiery tresses;
Showed the Death Dance of the spirits,
Warriors with their plumes and war clubs,
Flaring far away to the northward
In the frosty nights of Winter;
Showed the broad, white road in heaven,
Pathway of the ghosts, the shadows,
Running straight across the heavens,
Crowded with the ghosts, the shadows.

At the door on summer evenings
Sat the little Hiawatha,
Heard the whispering of the pine trees,
Heard the lapping of the waters,
Sounds of music, words of wonder;
"Minnie-wawa!" said the pine trees.
"Mudway-aushka!" said the water.

D.P.Lathrop—

Saw the firefly, Wah-wah-taysee,
Flitting through the dusk of evening,
With the twinkle of its candle
Lighting up the brakes and bushes,
And he sang the song of children,
Sang the song Nokomis taught him:
"Wah-wah-taysee, little firefly,
Little, flitting, white-fire insect,
Little, dancing, white-fire creature,
Light me with your little candle,
Ere upon my bed I lay me,
Ere in sleep I close my eyelids!"

Saw the moon rise from the water,
Rippling, rounding from the water,
Saw the flecks and shadows on it,
Whispered, "What is that, Nokomis?"
And the good Nokomis answered,
"Once a warrior, very angry,
Seized his grandmother, and threw her
Up into the sky at midnight;
Right against the moon he threw her;
'Tis her body that you see there."
Saw the rainbow in the heaven,
In the eastern sky, the rainbow,
Whispered, "What is that, Nokomis?"
And the good Nokomis answered:
" 'Tis the heaven of flowers you see there;
All the wild flowers of the forest,
All the lilies of the prairie,
When on earth they fade and perish,
Blossom in that heaven above us."

When he heard the owls at midnight,
Hooting, laughing in the forest,
"What is that?" he cried in terror;
"What is that?" he said, "Nokomis?"
And the good Nokomis answered:
"That is but the owl and owlet,
Talking in their native language,
Talking, scolding at each other."

Then the little Hiawatha
Learned of every bird its language,
Learned their names and all their secrets,
How they built their nests in Summer,
Where they hid themselves in Winter,
Talked with them whene'er he met them,
Called them "Hiawatha's Chickens."

Of all beasts he learned the language,
Learned their names and all their secrets,
How the beavers built their lodges,
Where the squirrels hid their acorns,
How the reindeer ran so swiftly,
Why the rabbit was so timid,
Talked with them whene'er he met them,
Called them "Hiawatha's Brothers."

HENRY WADSWORTH LONGFELLOW

COLUMBUS

BEHIND him lay the gray Azores,
    Behind, the Gates of Hercules;
Before him not the ghost of shores,
    Before him only shoreless seas.
The good mate said: "Now must we pray,
    For lo! the very stars are gone.
Brave Admiral, speak, what shall I say?"
    "Why, say 'Sail on! sail on! and on!' "

"My men grow mutinous day by day;
    My men grow ghastly wan and weak."
The stout mate thought of home; a spray
    Of salt wave washed his swarthy cheek.
"What shall I say, brave Admiral, say,
    If we sight naught but seas at dawn?"
"Why, you shall say at break of day,
    'Sail on! sail on! sail on! and on!' "

They sailed and sailed, as winds might blow,
   Until at last the blanched mate said:
"Why, now not even God would know
   Should I and all my men fall dead.
These very winds forget their way,
   For God from these dread seas is gone.
Now speak, brave Admiral, speak and say"—
   He said: "Sail on! sail on! and on!"

They sailed. They sailed. Then spake the mate:
   "This mad sea shows his teeth tonight.
He curls his lip, he lies in wait,
   With lifted teeth, as if to bite!
Brave Admiral, say but one good word:
   What shall we do when hope is gone?"
The words leapt like a leaping sword:
   "Sail on! sail on! sail on! and on!"

Then, pale and worn, he kept his deck,
   And peered through darkness. Ah, that night
Of all dark nights! And then a speck—
   A light! a light! a light! a light!
It grew, a starlit flag unfurled!
   It grew to be Time's burst of dawn.
He gained a world; he gave that world
   Its grandest lesson: "On! sail on!"

                    Joaquin Miller

PAUL REVERE'S RIDE

LISTEN, my children, and you shall hear
Of the midnight ride of Paul Revere,
On the eighteenth of April, in Seventy-five;
Hardly a man is now alive
Who remembers that famous day and year.

He said to his friend, "If the British march
By land or sea from the town tonight,
Hang a lantern aloft in the belfry arch
Of the North Church tower as a signal light,—
One, if by land, and two, if by sea;
And I on the opposite shore will be,
Ready to ride and spread the alarm
Through every Middlesex village and farm,
For the country folk to be up and to arm."

Then he said, "Good night!" and with muffled oar
Silently rowed to the Charlestown shore,
Just as the moon rose over the bay,
Where swinging wide at her moorings lay
The *Somerset,* British man-of-war;

A phantom ship, with each mast and spar
Across the moon like a prison bar,
And a huge black hulk, that was magnified
By its own reflection in the tide.

Meanwhile, his friend, through alley and street,
Wanders and watches with eager ears,
Till in the silence around him he hears
The muster of men at the barrack door,
The sound of arms, and the tramp of feet,
And the measured tread of the grenadiers,
Marching down to their boats on the shore.

Then he climbed the tower of the Old North Church,
By the wooden stairs, with stealthy tread,
To the belfry chamber overhead,
And startled the pigeons from their perch
On the somber rafters, that round him made
Masses and moving shapes of shade,—
By the trembling ladder, steep and tall,
To the highest window in the wall,
Where he paused to listen and look down
A moment on the roofs of the town,
And the moonlight flowing over all.

Beneath, in the churchyard, lay the dead,
In their night encampment on the hill,
Wrapped in silence so deep and still
That he could hear, like a sentinel's tread,
The watchful night wind, as it went
Creeping along from tent to tent,
And seeming to whisper, "All is well!"

LYND
WARD

A moment only he feels the spell
Of the place and the hour, and the secret dread
Of the lonely belfry and the dead;
For suddenly all his thoughts are bent
On a shadowy something far away,
Where the river widens to meet the bay,—
A line of black that bends and floats
On the rising tide, like a bridge of boats.

Meanwhile, impatient to mount and ride,
Booted and spurred, with a heavy stride
On the opposite shore walked Paul Revere.
Now he patted his horse's side,
Now gazed at the landscape far and near,
Then, impetuous, stamped the earth,
And turned and tightened his saddle girth;
But mostly he watched with eager search
The belfry tower of the Old North Church,
As it rose above the graves on the hill,
Lonely and spectral and somber and still.
And lo! as he looks, on the belfry's height
A glimmer, and then a gleam of light!
He springs to the saddle, the bridle he turns,
But lingers and gazes, till full on his sight,
A second lamp in the belfry burns!

A hurry of hoofs in a village street,
A shape in the moonlight, a bulk in the dark,
And beneath, from the pebbles, in passing, a spark
Struck out by a steed flying fearless and fleet:
That was all! And yet, through the gloom and the light,
The fate of a nation was riding that night;
And the spark struck out by that steed, in his flight,
Kindled the land into flame with its heat.

He has left the village and mounted the steep,
And beneath him, tranquil and broad and deep,
Is the Mystic, meeting the ocean tides;
And under the alders that skirt its edge,
Now soft on the sand, now loud on the ledge,
Is heard the tramp of his steed as he rides.

It was twelve by the village clock,
When he crossed the bridge into Medford town.
He heard the crowing of the cock,
And the barking of the farmer's dog,
And felt the damp of the river fog,
That rises after the sun goes down.

It was one by the village clock,
When he galloped into Lexington.
He saw the gilded weathercock
Swim in the moonlight as he passed,
And the meeting-house windows, blank and bare,
Gaze at him with a spectral glare,
As if they already stood aghast
At the bloody work they would look upon.

It was two by the village clock,
When he came to the bridge in Concord town.

He heard the bleating of the flock,
And the twitter of birds among the trees,
And felt the breath of the morning breeze
Blowing over the meadows brown.
And one was safe and asleep in his bed
Who at the bridge would be first to fall,
Who that day would be lying dead,
Pierced by a British musket ball.

You know the rest. In the books you have read
How the British Regulars fired and fled,—
How the farmers gave them ball for ball,
From behind each fence and farmyard wall,
Chasing the redcoats down the lane,
Then crossing the fields to emerge again
Under the trees at the turn of the road,
And only pausing to fire and load.

So through the night rode Paul Revere;
And so through the night went his cry of alarm
To every Middlesex village and farm,—
A cry of defiance and not of fear,
A voice in the darkness, a knock at the door,
And a word that shall echo forevermore!
For, borne on the night wind of the Past,
Through all our history, to the last,
In the hour of darkness and peril and need,
The people will waken and listen to hear
The hurrying hoof-beats of that steed
And the midnight message of Paul Revere.

HENRY WADSWORTH LONGFELLOW

184

YANKEE DOODLE

FATHER and I went down to camp,
  Along with Captain Goodwin,
And there we saw the men and boys
As thick as hasty puddin.'

Chorus. Yankee Doodle keep it up,
Yankee Doodle dandy,
Mind the music and the step,
And with the girls be handy.

And there was Captain Washington,
Upon a slapping stallion,
And giving orders to his men,
I guess there was a million.

And then the feathers on his hat,
They looked so 'tarnal finy
I wanted peskely to get,
To give to my Jemina.

And then they had a swamping gun,
As big as a log of maple,
On a deuced little cart,
A load for father's cattle.

LYND
WARD

CUMBERLAND GAP

CUMBERLAND GAP is a noted place,
  Cumberland Gap is a noted place,
Cumberland Gap is a noted place;
Three kinds of water for to wash your face.

Cumberland Gap with its cliff and rocks,
Cumberland Gap with its cliff and rocks,
Cumberland Gap with its cliff and rocks;
Home of the panther, and the bear and fox.

Daniel Boone stood on Pinnacle Rock,
Daniel Boone stood on Pinnacle Rock,
Daniel Boone stood on Pinnacle Rock;
He killed Indians with an old flintlock.

Lie down, boys, and take a little nap,
Lie down, boys, and take a little nap,
Lie down, boys, and take a little nap;
Fourteen miles to the Cumberland Gap.

CARL CARMER

Nino Carbe

DANIEL BOONE

WHEN Daniel Boone goes by, at night,
    The phantom deer arise
And all lost, wild America
Is burning in their eyes.
    ROSEMARY and STEPHEN VINCENT BENÉT

Nino Carbe

WASHINGTON

HE PLAYED by the river when he was young,
He raced with rabbits along the hills,
He fished for minnows, and climbed and swung,
And hooted back at the whippoorwills.
Strong and slender and tall he grew
And then, one morning, the bugles blew.

Over the hills, the summons came,
Over the river's shining rim.
He said that the bugles called his name,
He knew that his country needed him,
And he answered, "Coming!" and marched away
For many a night and many a day.

Perhaps when the marches were hot and long
He'd think of the river flowing by,
Or, camping under the winter sky,
Would hear the whippoorwill's far-off song.
At work, at play, in peace or strife,
He loved America all his life!

NANCY BYRD TURNER

LINCOLN

THERE was a boy of other days,
A quiet, awkward, earnest lad,
Who trudged long weary miles to get
A book on which his heart was set—
And then no candle had!

He was too poor to buy a lamp
But very wise in woodmen's ways.
He gathered seasoned bough and stem,
And crisping leaf, and kindled them
Into a ruddy blaze.

Then as he lay full length and read,
The firelight flickered on his face,
And etched his shadow on the gloom,
And made a picture in the room,
In that most humble place.

The hard years came, the hard years went,
But, gentle, brave, and strong of will,
He met them all. And when today
We see his pictured face, we say,
"There's light upon it still."

NANCY BYRD TURNER

Corinne Dillon

WESTERN WAGONS

THEY went with axe and rifle,
   when the trail was still to blaze,
They went with wife and children,
   in the prairie-schooner days,
With banjo and with frying pan—
   Susanna, don't you cry!
For I'm off to California
   to get rich out there or die!

We've broken land and cleared it,
   but we're tired of where we are.
They say that wild Nebraska
   is a better place by far.
There's gold in far Wyoming,
   there's black earth in Ioway,
So pack up the kids and blankets,
   for we're moving out today!

190

The cowards never started
  and the weak died on the road,
And all across the continent
  the endless campfires glowed.
We'd taken land and settled—
  but a traveler passed by—
And we're going West tomorrow—
  Lordy, never ask us why!

We're going West tomorrow,
  where the promises can't fail.
O'er the hills in legions, boys,
  and crowd the dusty trail!
We shall starve and freeze and suffer.
  We shall die, and tame the lands.
But we're going West tomorrow,
  with our fortune in our hands.

ROSEMARY and STEPHEN VINCENT BENÉT

APPLE-SEED JOHN

POOR Johnny was bended well-nigh double
    With years of toil, and care, and trouble;
But his large old heart still felt the need
Of doing for others some kindly deed.

"But what can I do," old Johnny said:
"I who work so hard for daily bread?
It takes heaps of money to do much good;
I am far too poor to do as I would."

The old man sat thinking deeply awhile,
Then over his features gleamed a smile,
And he clapped his hands with a boyish glee,
And said to himself: "There's a way for me!"

He worked, and he worked with might and main,
But no one knew the plan in his brain.
He took ripe apples in pay for chores,
And carefully cut from them all the cores.

He filled a bag full, then wandered away,
And no man saw him for many a day.
With knapsack over his shoulder slung,
He marched along, and whistled or sung.

He seemed to roam with no object in view,
Like one who had nothing on earth to do;
But, journeying thus o'er the prairies wide,
He paused now and then, and his bag untied.

With pointed cane deep holes he would bore,
And in every hole he placed a core;
Then covered them well, and left them there
In keeping of sunshine, rain, and air.

Sometimes for days he waded through grass,
And saw not a living creature pass,
But often, when sinking to sleep in the dark,
He heard the owls hoot and the prairie dogs bark.

Sometimes an Indian of sturdy limb
Came striding along and walked with him;
And he who had food shared with the other,
As if he had met a hungry brother.

When the Indian saw how the bag was filled,
And looked at the holes that the white man drilled,
He thought to himself 'twas a silly plan.
To be planting seed for some future man.

Sometimes a log cabin came in view,
Where Johnny was sure to find jobs to do,
By which he gained stores of bread and meat,
And welcome rest for his weary feet.

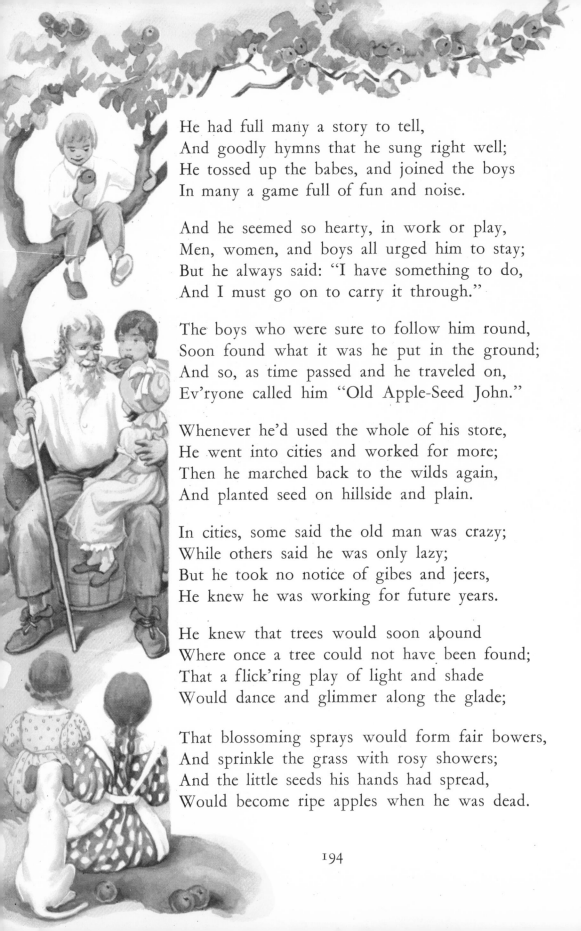

He had full many a story to tell,
And goodly hymns that he sung right well;
He tossed up the babes, and joined the boys
In many a game full of fun and noise.

And he seemed so hearty, in work or play,
Men, women, and boys all urged him to stay;
But he always said: "I have something to do,
And I must go on to carry it through."

The boys who were sure to follow him round,
Soon found what it was he put in the ground;
And so, as time passed and he traveled on,
Ev'ryone called him "Old Apple-Seed John."

Whenever he'd used the whole of his store,
He went into cities and worked for more;
Then he marched back to the wilds again,
And planted seed on hillside and plain.

In cities, some said the old man was crazy;
While others said he was only lazy;
But he took no notice of gibes and jeers,
He knew he was working for future years.

He knew that trees would soon abound
Where once a tree could not have been found;
That a flick'ring play of light and shade
Would dance and glimmer along the glade;

That blossoming sprays would form fair bowers,
And sprinkle the grass with rosy showers;
And the little seeds his hands had spread,
Would become ripe apples when he was dead.

So he kept on traveling far and wide,
Till his old limbs failed him, and he died.
He said at the last: "'Tis a comfort to feel
I've done good in the world, though not a great deal."

Weary travelers, journeying west,
In the shade of his trees find pleasant rest;
And they often start, with glad surprise,
At the rosy fruit that round them lies.

And if they inquire whence came such trees,
Where not a bough once swayed in the breeze,
The answer still comes, as they travel on:
"These trees were planted by Apple-Seed John."

LYDIA MARIA CHILD

AMERICA

MY country, 'tis of thee,
  Sweet land of liberty,
Of thee I sing.
Land where my fathers died!
Land of the Pilgrims' pride
From every mountainside,
  Let freedom ring!

My native country, thee,
Land of the noble free,
  Thy name I love.
I love thy rocks and rills,
Thy woods and templed hills;
My heart with rapture thrills
  Like that above.

Let music swell the breeze,
And ring from all the trees
  Sweet freedom's song.
Let mortal tongues awake,
Let all that breathe partake,
Let rocks their silence break,
  The sound prolong.

Our fathers' God, to Thee,
Author of liberty,
  To Thee we sing.
Long may our land be bright
With freedom's holy light;
Protect us by Thy might,
  Great God, our King.

SAMUEL FRANCIS SMITH

THE MAPLE LEAF FOREVER

IN DAYS of yore, from Britain's shore,
Wolfe, the dauntless hero came,
And planted firm Britannia's flag
On Canada's fair domain!
Here may it wave, our boast, our pride,
And joined in love together,
The Thistle, Shamrock, Rose entwine,
The Maple Leaf forever!
　　The Maple Leaf, our emblem dear,
　　The Maple Leaf forever!
　　God save our King, and Heaven bless
　　The Maple Leaf forever!

At Queenston Heights and Lundy's Lane,
Our brave fathers, side by side,
For freedom, homes, and loved ones dear
Firmly stood and nobly died.
And those dear rights which they maintained,
We swear to yield them never!
Our watchword ever more shall be,
The Maple Leaf forever!
　　The Maple Leaf, our emblem dear,
　　The Maple Leaf forever!
　　God save our King, and Heaven bless
　　The Maple Leaf forever.

ALEXANDER MUIR

A HOME ON THE RANGE
(Cowboy Song)

OH, give me a home where the buffalo roam,
    Where the deer and the antelope play;
Where seldom is heard a discouraging word
    And the skies are not cloudy all day.

Chorus: Home, home on the range,
    Where the deer and the antelope play;
Where seldom is heard a discouraging word
    And the skies are not cloudy all day.

Where the air is so pure, the zephyrs so free,
    The breezes so balmy and light,
That I would not exchange my home on the range
    For all the cities so bright.

The red man was pressed from this part of the West,
    He's likely no more to return
To the banks of Red River where seldom if ever
    Their flickering campfires burn.

How often at night when the heavens are bright
  With the light from the glittering stars,
Have I stood here amazed and asked as I gazed
  If their glory exceeds that of ours.

Oh, I love these wild flowers in this dear land of ours;
  The curlew I love to hear scream;
And I love the white rocks and the antelope flocks
  That graze on the mountaintops green.

Oh, give me a land where the bright diamond sand
  Flows leisurely down the stream;
Where the graceful white swan goes gliding along
  Like a maid in a heavenly dream.

Then I would not exchange my home on the range,
  Where the deer and the antelope play;
Where seldom is heard a discouraging word
  And the skies are not cloudy all day.

Chorus: Home, home on the range,
  Where the deer and the antelope play;
Where seldom is heard a discouraging word
  And the skies are not cloudy all day.

Samuel Armstrong

SHE'LL BE COMIN' ROUND THE MOUNTAIN

(A Mountain Ballad)

SHE'LL be comin' round the mountain,
 When she comes.
She'll be comin' round the mountain,
 When she comes.
She'll be comin' round the mountain,
She'll be comin' round the mountain,
She'll be comin' round the mountain,
 When she comes.

She'll be drivin' six white horses,
 When she comes.
She'll be drivin' six white horses,
 When she comes.
She'll be drivin' six white horses,
She'll be drivin' six white horses,
She'll be drivin' six white horses,
 When she comes.

Oh we'll all go to meet her,
 When she comes.
Oh we'll all go to meet her,
 When she comes.
We will kill the old red rooster,
We will kill the old red rooster,
And we'll all have chicken and dumplin',
 When she comes.

200

Nino Carbe

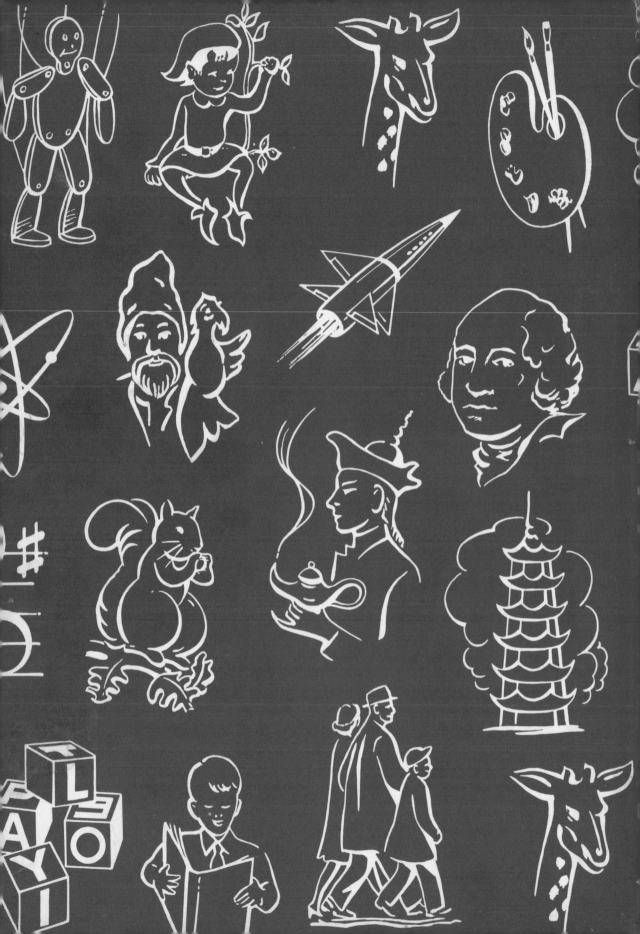